In this issu

Editor's introduction

William Gray

I n this bicentenary year of Grimms' *Fairy Tales* (*Kinder- und Hausmärchen* was first published in December 1812) the second issue of *Gramarye* begins with a discussion between children's literature expert Nick Tucker and folklore expert Jacqueline Simpson about the suitability of fairy tales for children. This is the continuation of a dialogue begun on BBC Radio 4's Today programme last February. Nick also addressed these issues last year in a Sussex Centre public lecture entitled 'Fairy Tales in Print: A Troubled History'.

This timely debate is followed by a beautifully illustrated article by Anne Anderson celebrating the work of faerie illustrator Brian Froud, whose latest illustrated book, *Trolls*, has just appeared. We have also had the rare opportunity to do a wide-ranging interview with Brian, which covers his sources, his inspirations and his plans.

For me one of the highlights of the Folklore and Fantasy Conference that the Sussex Centre ran with the Folklore Society at the University of Chichester last April was Angelika Rüdiger's paper on the historical and cultural transformations of mythical Welsh hero 'Gwyn ap Nudd'. Angelika has prepared a revised version of her fascinating paper for this issue of *Gramarye*, and we've been fortunate to get permission to use not only one of Margaret Jones's magical illustrations of Welsh mythology, but also one of Alan Lee's fabulous illustrations of the *Mabinogion*.

Next we have another speaker from the Folklore and Fantasy Conference, Kate Forsyth, the Australian fantasy author best known for *The Witches of Eileanan* and *Rhiannon's Ride* series. Just in time for Christmas, Kate retells a traditional German folktale already retold in the mid-19th century as 'The Christmas Fairy of Strasburg' by J. Stirling Coyne. Kate's sparkling new version is entitled 'Count Stoneheart and the First Christmas Tree'.

Continuing our series featuring fairy-tale writers and scholars describing a life-shaping early reading (or listening) experience of a fairy tale, we have a contribution by Martine Hennard Dutheil de la Rochère of the University of Lausanne, Switzerland. As in Maria Nikolajeva's piece in the last issue of *Gramarye*, it is again Hans Christian Andersen's writing that left a lasting impression on the young Martine.

At the launch of *Gramarye* last May we were enthralled by Steve O'Brien reading 'The Lennan Sidh', from his brilliant new collection of stories entitled *The Oldest Tales*. Besides leading the MA in Creative Writing at the University of Portsmouth, Steve is a widely published poet and editor of the *London Magazine*, Britain's oldest literary journal.

After some agonising, the story we have selected from *The Oldest Tales* for this issue of *Gramarye* is entitled 'Herne'. We are doubly fortunate to have received permission from Melvyn Grant to include his terrifying illustration 'Hearne', which some readers may remember from the cover of the old Puffin edition of Susan Cooper's *The Dark is Rising* (the present writer was certainly haunted by it).

Next there's something completely different: Dr Louise Jolly is a qualified academic in the area of cultural history who also works as a writer and analyst in marketing and advertising. She says she is fascinated by the way the cultural unconscious surfaces in advertising. Her intriguing article about the place of fantasy and the supernatural in advertising is entitled: 'Whatever happened to the pixies? The shrinking role of Snap, Crackle and Pop in British Rice Krispies advertising'.

If the folklore of England and Wales has been prominent in this issue of *Gramarye* – we've had to postpone Pat Ryan's excellent article on the Irish folktale 'The Well of D'Yerree-in-Dowan' till the next issue because of lack of space – Scottish folklore appears in the Reviews section with a review by Sophia Kingshill (co-author with the late Jennifer Westwood of *The Lore of Scotland*) of a new edition of *Traditional Tales* by Alan Cunningham, friend and colleague of Sir Walter Scott and James Hogg, 'the Ettrick Shepherd'. Since this issue of *Gramarye* is rich in illustrations, it's worth mentioning that the cover image of Cunningham's book is the splendid 'Galloway Idyll' by Glasgow Boy E.A. Hornel. We also have reviews of new books on Lewis Carroll (by Colin Manlove), on the Twilight series (by Malini Roy) and *On Monsters: An Unnatural History of Our Worst Fears* (by Miles Leeson).

And finally, talking of monsters: if not exactly a monster read, then this latest issue of *Gramarye* is certainly rather fatter than the first issue, whose slimness was a cause of some regret to the kind reviewer in Cabinet des Fées, who gently chastened us for offering too little of a good thing!

· ·

Professor William Gray

Bill Gray

Arthur Rackham, 'O waken, waken, Burd Isbel', from 'Young Beichan', Child Ballad.

To tell or not to tell: are fairy tales suitable for children?

Nicholas Tucker and Jacqueline Simpson

A discussion between children's literature expert Nick Tucker and folklore expert Jacqueline Simpson about the suitability of fairy tales for children. This is the continuation of a dialogue begun on BBC Radio 4's Today programme last February.

Nicholas Tucker

The chief fear aroused by fairy tales these days is that not enough children are encouraged to read them. Lauded by psychoanalysts from Freud onwards for their understanding of the human psyche, affectionately recalled in legions of autobiographies, beautifully illustrated by generations of brilliant artists, turned into plays, operas or ballets, and reinterpreted by adult novelists, they are seen today as an invaluable European treasure-house of the imagination that should continue to have as wide a readership as possible.

I too have read or told fairy tales to children at home or in school over the years, and can attest to how well they still work. But there are also elements to them that I dislike. Stories that have survived in an oral culture for so long before eventually being written down and published must contain matter of enduring relevance and interest to the human imagination. But what if there are elements in this same imagination better not served or encouraged by literature? Humans over the centuries, for example, have found deformity a matter for cruel humour. Does this mean it is therefore acceptable to continue lampooning the bent, the ugly or the deformed in fairy tales, as some of them still do, both in print and in accompanying illustrations?

Carl Jung once opined that the German veneration of Hitler at the time was a reflection of the eternal human fantasy of a great leader arriving on the scene to lead us out of all our troubles – the plot of so many myths and fairy tales. Such plots are universal – think of the traditional cowboy film. But how often do children have access to stories that question this heroic myth? As it is, committees, town councils, government advisors or any other more or less representational body nearly always receive short shrift in heroic literature from fairy tales to the sagas of Tolkien. Far better allow the leader, whoever he – or, rarely, she – is, to work everything out on their own or along with a small body of equally heroic friends. Would young readers ever guess from such reading that organisations such as the Red Cross or Médecins Sans Frontières put their names to collective achievements every bit as heroic and brave? Or that brave leaders today sometimes turn into unelected dictators tomorrow? Such issues are often taken on by modern children's writers, but fairy tales remain stuck in a heroic groove that needs far more questioning from other sources outside the genre.

And what about the rampant sexism in fairy tales? It is idle to deny its existence, and attempts by modern writers to come up with non-sexist fairy tales have seldom succeeded. I still believe that children have a right to such tales. There can be something deliciously regressive in escaping into a story embodying patently out-of-date images when in real life females of any age know that they have now to be responsible for themselves and make their own way regardless of beauty or wealth. But fairy tales embodying such passive approaches should at the least be balanced by other stories suggesting more positive attitudes.

Past critics of fairy tales tend to be dismissed for their lack of understanding or humour but what they had to say at the time was often quite sensible. When the great Italian educationalist Maria Montessori wrote that children under seven should not have access to fairy tales, this was against a cultural background when they often had access to little else. Feeding small children with an exclusive diet of fantasy is surely questionable. Years later, Professors John and Elizabeth Newson also roundly condemned what they termed 'bamboozlement' in the parenting practices they were examining among largely working-class families in Nottingham in the 1960s (Newson and Newson 1968). By this they meant a diet of misinformation or denial fed to children whenever they asked questions thought either difficult or potentially embarrassing. At around the same time the American psychologists Robert Hess and Virginia Shipman coined the phrase 'the meaning of deprivation is the deprivation of meaning' in their seminal paper *Early Experience and the Socialization of Cognitive Modes in Children* (Hess and Shipman 1965).

Are fairy tales also guilty of depriving small children of meaning? Hardly, because they do not set out to tell the literal truth. Their proper realm is with human dreams and fantasy, and most young readers quickly come to understand this. But there is also an enduring role for stories from which children can learn more about the world's realities. Fairy tales are not enough in themselves. Their early critics made this point even more forcefully at a time when there was little or no realistic fiction around for young readers to act as a counterweight.

Critics were also surely justified in condemning the way fairy tales sometimes enshrined and indeed propagated superstition. Creating realistically wicked witches in stories was a different matter at a time when belief in witchcraft remained widespread. No wonder this caused pain to enlightened liberals who hated how these primitive beliefs continued to be supported by children's favourite reading matter. This concern is still not an entirely closed issue. Would a primary school teacher read out a fairy story about witches to a class containing recent immigrants from Uganda, where witchcraft beliefs are still current? Would any British publisher try to sell fairy tales that included witches to present-day Ugandan schools with an easy conscience?

Today compilers and publishers treat fairy tales as a rich, out-of-copyright store selected from and often altered at will for whatever version of the tales best suits contemporary sensitivities. This process started with the brothers Grimm, happy to rewrite some of the more savage fairy tales while omitting others considered too gross even then. Other early anthologists, like Sir George Dasent in his great collection *Popular Tales from the Norse*, retained some of the rougher, more earthy stories. But for Dasent this meant also including two comically defensive prefaces warning young readers – on their honour – not to look at these tales themselves. History does not record whether a single child ever obeyed this injunction.

Modern publishers often include more gruesome stories like the Grimms' *The Juniper Tree*, omitted for most of the 20th century. Older readers will have no problems with stories like this. But there are many accounts of small children scared almost out of their wits in the past by particularly frightening stories, especially those warning them of the dire consequences of not staying quietly in their beds during the night. This was a favourite way for some mothers or nursemaids to ensure they had some peace for themselves during the evenings at a time when goodnight stories were as much an arm of adult discipline as an opportunity for loving bonding. Small children today can still be frightened by stories, fairy or otherwise, that threaten to overload their sometimes fragile state of self-confidence. Any parent misjudging the potential effect on an infant of, say, *Hansel and Gretel* or *Babes in the Wood* could still be in for some troubled nights to follow.

What about traditional fairy story settings? For John Ruskin, in his 1868 essay 'Fairy Stories':

> All the best fairy tales have owed their birth, and the greater part of their power, to narrowness of social circumstances: they belonged properly to districts in which walled cities are surrounded by bright and unblemished country, and in which a healthy and bustling town life, not highly refined, is relieved by, and contrasted with, the calm enchantment of pastoral and woodland scenery, either under humble cultivation by peasant masters, or left to its natural solitude.

Today, these rural settings are increasingly distant from the day-to-day realities of most children in the developed world. This could for some remain part of their enduring appeal, but children also want at least some stories set in the world they know.

Yet comforting stereotypes of past rural life have always played an important part in art and fiction. Charming and seductive, they nevertheless disguise the harsher realities of pre-industrial times. While fairy stories often mention poverty there is normally a happy ending when such concerns no longer seem an issue. This worship of extreme wealth for its own sake is not a pretty sight – does a fairy-tale hero ever share out the fortune he comes into rather than immediately joining the ruling class that had previously kept him poor and will continue to do the same to the less fortunate? For Marxist critic Jack Zipes, 'In all Grimms' fairy tales, male domination and master-slave relationships are rationalized so long as the rulers are benevolent and use their power justly. If tyrants and parents are challenged, they relent or are replaced, but the property relationships and patriarchy are not transformed' (Zipes 1983).

Preaching acceptance rather than protest, protecting the social status quo by occasionally making a few cosmetic changes at the top – these stories can only contemplate change that comes through either magic or luck. Such are the immemorial fantasies of the poor and dispossessed with no expectation in their own lives of ever changing their condition. Thankfully, modern children have other literature to hand advocating more positive attitudes to challenging an unjust social order.

The regular appearance of royalty in fairy tales is another aspect of their inherent conservatism. Beautiful princesses and handsome princes are regularly held up as romantic ideals, although once they appear as mature kings and queens in succeeding stories after an initial spell of 'living happily ever after' they often no longer seem quite so contented. Luxuriating in fantasies about the rich and attractive is part of the essence of fantasy. But there should also be other books around offering radically different points of view along with some changes in cast. Step-parents, for example, always receive such a bad press in fairy tales at a time when there are more around than ever before. Other stories painting step-parents in a better light would do something to redress this balance.

Walt Disney – usually excoriated by those who love traditional fairy tales – has in fact done many of these stories a singular service over the years. Introducing tuneful music, jokes and contemporary accents to his fairy story films has made these tales newly accessible to young audiences who might otherwise have started seeing them as somewhat quaint and antique. Just as the Grimm brothers polished up fairy tales mainly drawn – as they thought – from the oral tradition, so has Disney made some of the same tales more accessible to modern audiences.

And I am glad that he has. Because for all their faults, at their best traditional fairy tales remain wonderful stories and often have something to tell us that is wise at one moment and consoling the next. But I would also contend that they have been allowed an uncritical ride for too long now. Some of them are really not as nice as you might remember and they do need to be balanced by other sorts of children's literature doing something quite different.

References
Hess, R.D. and Shipman, V.C., 'Early Experience and the Socialization of Cognitive Modes in Children', *Child Development*, 36 (University of Chicago, 1965), pp.869-86.
Newson, John and Elizabeth, *Four Years Old in an Urban Community* (London: Penguin, 1968)
Zipes, Jack, *Fairy Tales and the Art of Subversion* (New York: Routledge, 1983), p.59.

· ·

Jacqueline Simpson

I'm probably not the right person to discuss Nick Tucker's article, for I have no children or grandchildren, and as a teacher I dealt only with teenagers, so I have never been in a position to watch how the very young react to fairy tales. All I can do is summon up memories of my own reactions, and they only reach back to when I was five or six, not to earliest childhood.

I can certainly agree that a child's fears and prejudices grow out of early impressions drawn from fiction (including fairy tales) as well as from real life, but I doubt that it is desirable, or indeed possible, to eliminate all negative imagery and associations by resorting to censorship. Nick Tucker does not in fact demand this; his point, a wiser and more practical one, is simply to ensure that some positives are available as a counter-balance. I can readily agree, with back-up from my own recollections. For instance, I encountered Captain Hook in *Peter Pan* a year or two earlier than Captain Cuttle in *Dombey and Son*, but the latter has ensured that I am not scared or disgusted by hooks in real life, even though horror films and James Bond thrillers regularly use them as indicators of evil.

I suspect that negative stereotyping in fiction will have little effect unless reinforced by social attitudes and real-life experience. Thus, black people are threatening figures in the *Arabian Nights*, but for me this was far outweighed by admiration for Paul Robeson's voice and for Jesse Owens in the film of the 1936 Olympics. On the other hand, the mockery of a Jew in one of the Grimms' tales fitted in perfectly with the casual scornful anti-Semitism so widespread in Britain in the 1930s, and so I accepted it without a second thought. As for wicked stepmothers and mothers-in-law, jealous half-sisters, and murderous uncles, I don't think it ever occurred to me that I might encounter one in real life; but then, I was an only child in a stable nuclear family, and

I am sadly aware that others are less lucky than I was. For them, such stereotypes might well engender fears and suspicions.

However, though you can vary the type of figure representing evil in your fairy tales, you cannot eliminate evil itself, for narrative requires contrast, or even conflict. Moreover, traditional fairy tales carry moral messages about courage, persistence, patience, kindness, generosity, and so forth, virtues which shine out best when set against evil and danger. Their courageous optimism is summed up in a famous saying attributed to G.K. Chesterton: 'Fairy tales don't tell children dragons exist. Children already know dragons exist. Fairy tales tell children that the dragons can be killed.'

Related to this is the concept of justice, of fairness, so important in children's minds. As they themselves are so frequently scolded and punished, they demand that in their stories 'the good end happily *and the bad unhappily*' (Wilde's definition of fiction in *The Importance of Being Ernest*). At any rate, I did. I was positively delighted when wicked queens were forced to dance to death in red-hot shoes or rolled down steep hills inside a spiked barrel, as happened in my unexpurgated 19th-century edition of Grimm. But I was disgusted and upset by the fate of Andersen's Little Mermaid, which I saw as sheer cruelty – turning into some sort of semi-angel was, to my mind, no compensation for the injustice of losing the prince for whom she had sacrificed so much. Indeed, rejection and injustice is such a recurrent theme in Andersen that there was little apart from the Ugly Duckling that I could read with pleasure, and the book mostly lay unopened. Similarly, I was eight when I saw the *Wizard of Oz*, and I vividly remember how the whole film was ruined for me by its ending – it's *unfair*, I wailed, we've been so looking forward to meeting this wonderful wizard, and it turns out he's an old fraud; and as for Dorothy, she just asks to go home! How stupid, how boring is that! Nowadays, of course, I realise that Andersen was a paranoid masochist, and that Frank L. Baum had an agenda, to debunk the concept of God. At the time, I simply thought they wrote very feeble and unpleasant stories. Authentic traditional fairy tales never cheated my expectation of justice in this way.

Nick Tucker has raised three issues: that the total repertoire of tales to which a child is exposed should strike a balance between fantasy and realism; that the moral and social messages they convey should be acceptable by the criteria of our own times; and that some tales are too frightening for very young children. As regards the first, this balance is indeed a healthy one, but can there really be many children for whom it is lacking – who grow up knowing *only* fairy tales, or *only* stories about the everyday world around them? As for the second, I would contend that fairy tales teach many virtues that are, or should be, still valid and desirable in our time; their chief flaw is their sexism, which the story-telling parent or teacher can counteract by encouraging a little girl to identify herself with the active, questing hero rather than the passive 'princess' he seeks or rescues. As for frightening stories, if the parent or teacher is *telling* the story, rather than reading it from a book, and if she or he has a smidgen of common sense, she/he will observe the child's reaction, and drop that particular tale from the repertoire. Fairy tales, after all, were meant for telling, and what is told will shift and change a little as it goes, to suit the needs and tastes of teller and hearers alike.

Adelaide Claxton,
'Wonderland'.

13

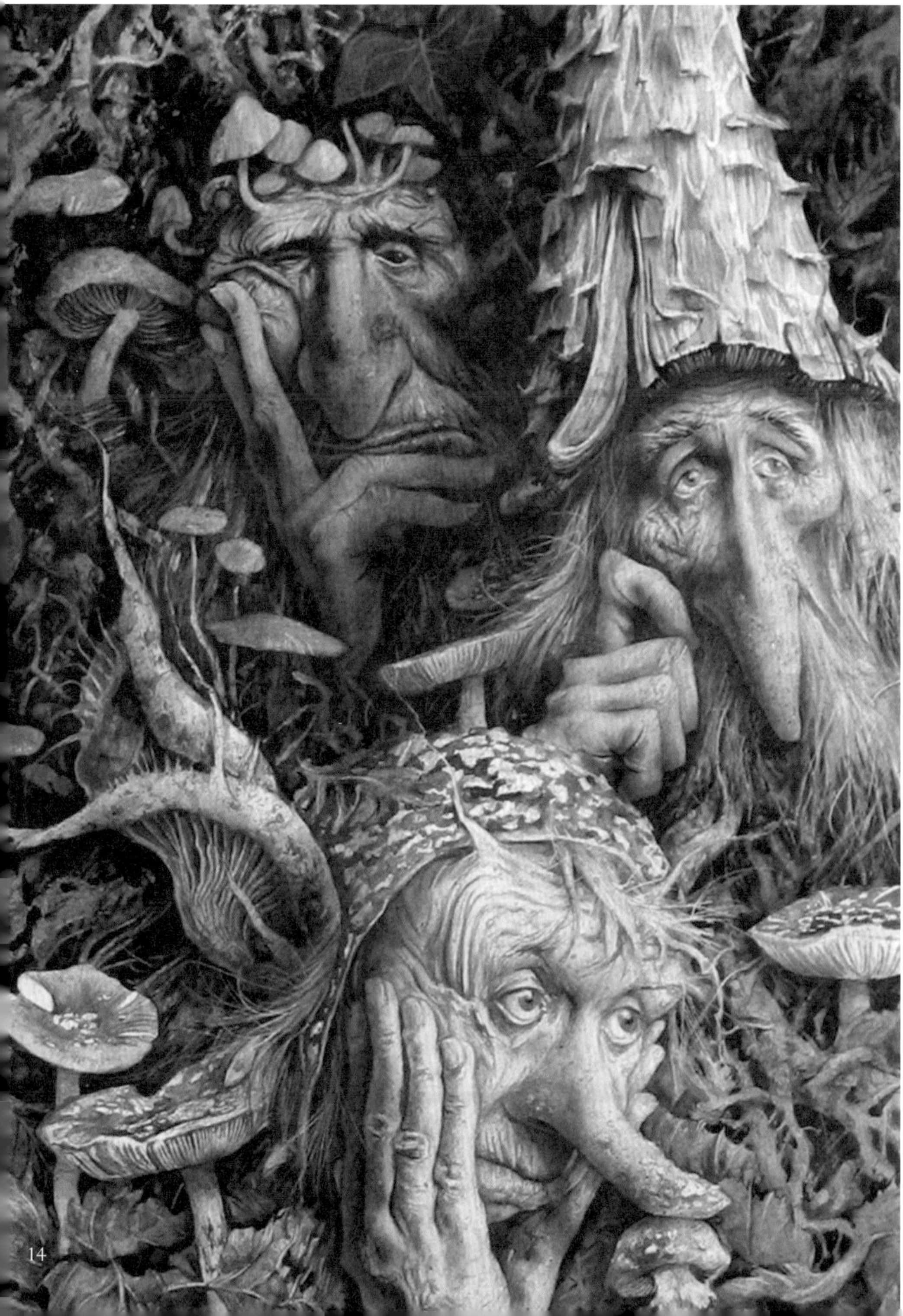

Fig. 1 'Gnomes', *The Land of Froud* (1977). Credit: Brian Froud.

A singular vision:
Brian Froud's faerie world

Anne Anderson

F or Brian Froud (b. 1947) faeries really do exist, but they do not reside at the bottom of his garden; they have always lived in his imagination. In truth his imagination is fired by Dartmoor; he and his wife, model-maker Wendy Froud, have lived in the picturesque village of Chagford since the 1970s. Dartmoor exudes mystery; its nooks and crannies may be home to all manner of creatures. As we cross the windswept hills, Froud's mischievous goblins or beautiful fairies may be observing us from the roots of a tree or a rocky outcrop. Like her father, Jim Henson, creator of the Muppets, Cheryl Henson has also been seduced by Froud's creations: 'deep in a primeval forest, I too would like to be a Froud Fairy'.[1]

Froud's World of Faerie is close at hand, firmly linked to the natural world; he reveals the unseen, 'a more expansive view of our own world, revealing places, people and experiences we might otherwise perceive'.[2] Hence Froud resists the label of 'fantasy artist', claiming:

> My art is a direct expression of how the world is to me. I imagine then the world is a living entity with a soul of profound depth and beauty. Faeries are an expression of aspects of this soul. They are sparks of the inner spiritual light of the world. A sketchbook for me is an exploration and a record of my search to touch and experience this light.[3]

While the artist who draws from life uses a sketchbook to record what he observes, Froud attempts to delineate what cannot be seen directly. To see faeries we have to believe in them; Froud has tutored us in *How to See Faeries* (2011) for over thirty years. His vision inspired the films 'The Dark Crystal' (1982) and 'Labyrinth' (1986), on which he worked as the conceptual designer in conjunction with Jim Henson's Creature Shop. He collaborated with Terry Jones, a screenwriter on 'Labyrinth', publishing *The Goblins of Labyrinth* (1986, reissued in abridged form as *The Goblin Companion: A Field Guide to Goblins*, 1996). A further collaboration resulted in the Lady Cottington series, initiated with *Lady Cottington's Pressed Fairy Book* (1994). *The Runes of Elfland* (2003) was in partnership with Ari Berk, Professor of Myth and Folklore, Central Michigan University. Recent publications include *The Heart of*

Faerie Oracle, authored by his wife, and *How To See Faeries* with *New York Times* best-selling author John Matthews. Froud is worthy to take his place in the long lineage of artists who have imagined faerie: Henry Fuseli, Richard Dadd, George Cruikshank, Daniel Maclise, Richard 'Dickey' Doyle, John Anster Fitzgerald, Joseph Noel Paton, Arthur Rackham and Edmund Dulac. Clearly Froud has drawn on these illustrious precursors but he has forged his own inimitable style. Heidi Leigh, curator of Animazing Gallery, claims Froud is 'the most important faerie artist of our time'.[4]

Froud, in partnership with Alan Lee (b. 1947), is said to have rekindled the interest in faerie and fantasy art with *Faeries* (1978). As in any collaboration, compromise was a necessity: 'We traded ... Alan would give me a nasty goblin if I'd sacrifice a noseless brownie. We tried to fix it so each of us would have his share of nasty and pretty ones. The nasty ones, of course, are always much more fun.'[5] The partners hold each other in mutual respect: Froud considers Lee 'a magnificent watercolourist, a master of his medium', while Lee deems Froud 'superb at highly detailed work and bursting with vision and vitality'. In personality and style they balanced each other, with Lee the introvert and Froud the extravert: 'It makes a nice mix,' declared Lee. 'I quieten him down; he livens me up.'[6] Together they redefined the traditional view of faeries as sweet and childlike, drawing on Victorian masters, notably Doyle, Rackham and Charles and Heath Robinson. As Heidi Leigh observes, in Froud's vision sensual beauty collides with the ugly and grotesque, while the serene jostles with the comedic. Froud embraces the paradox of faerie, which can be both halcyon and disquieting, as seen in *Good Faeries, Bad Faeries* (1998): 'he reveals the world of Faeries as he sees it, with no tempering filter or predilection for the safe and secure'.[7] As Froud warns, 'It is wise to remember that faeries are not only good'.[8]

Faeries appeared at a judicious moment: late 1970s pop culture saw a revival of interest in the Pre-Raphaelites and Art Nouveau. Student walls were covered with posters by Alphonse Mucha (1860-1939) and Aubrey Beardsley (1872-98). With his style synthesising Pre-Raphaelitism, notably the paintings of Edward Burne-Jones (1833-98), and the Golden Age of illustration, exemplified by Arthur Rackham (1867-1939), Froud is both a product and shaping influence of the 'flower-power' era.

Froud's faeries appear to spring fully formed in *The Land of Froud* (1977; Fig. 1), but they were a product of his youth and education. Born in Winchester, Hampshire, his family moved to Kent where he attended Maidstone College of Art. He began in the painting school but gravitated to graphic design, as this offered wider scope for his imagination:

> There is a mystery in how a simple line can be so expressive
> of emotional intent. Just pencil and paper, a colour wash –
> all pretensions of grandeur are set aside. This can have a directness
> and honesty that can be more elusive in a more elaborate
> confection of paint, canvas and fancy frame. The outside form
> must reveal the inner truth.[9]

Froud is a superb draughtsman, his preference for the bounding line no doubt inspired by Beardsley and Rackham, who transformed the graphic arts at the turn of the 20th century. Both combined beauty with the grotesque and laced their images with humorous asides. Froud openly acknowledges his debt to Rackham:

> There are many pioneers of Faerie exploration – storytellers, playwrights, writers, painters, illustrators – but the most influential for me was Arthur Rackham … Rackham's drawings of trees with faces reminded me of how I felt when I was young – that there was an inner life to nature and that everything had its own intense personality … Most of all, it was his juxtaposition of the grotesque and the beautiful that intrigued me. But it was his sinewy, organic line, which spoke of the certainty that humankind and nature were seamlessly bonded, that really inspired me. Thank you, Mr Rackham, for reminding me that I live in a natural world inhabited by a personified consciousness; that I live in a world of Faerie.[10]

'Personified consciousness' enables Froud to both animate and imbue nature with symbolic resonance; he sees the spirit that animates trees and plants. He draws on mythology and folklore to authenticate his vision. Both Froud and Lee have turned to Rackham, whose trees are distinctly anthropomorphised, drawing on the long tradition of the Dryad; when his trees don round spectacles, as seen on the frontispiece to Grimm's *Little Brother* and *Little Sister* (1917), they seem to resemble Rackham himself! Perhaps these spectacles allude to venerable age and wisdom; in *Somebody's Book*, an illustration for 'The Windmill' (1923), a bespectacled tree leans over the reader as if following the text.[11] Rackham's trees can be seen at their best in 'The Trees and the Axe' from Aesop's *Fables* (1912); they are indebted to Burne-Jones' 'Briar Rose' series (1885-90, Buscot Park), most notably the first in the sequence, 'The Briar Wood'.[12] Laurence Housman's (1865-1959) edition of Christina Rossetti's *Goblin Market* (1893) contributed to the evolution of the 'spooky' tree, whose branches resemble limbs. While Lee conjured the Ents for *Lord of the Rings*, Froud creates richly wooded forests teeming with both beautiful and bizarre creatures (Fig. 2).

These hidden 'Faces in the Forest' are ever close, yet tantalisingly beyond reach. Froud believes faeries speak the ancient language of the land; to hear and interpret what they say inspires his images: 'What do the sinuous shapes of branch and trunk have to tell me? And the river's song? Why do I feel this way about the moss-softened rocks?'[13] In the woods the veil between our world and Faerie becomes thin, allowing a glimpse across the threshold or behind the mask.

An intrinsic facet of the wild woods, faeries exist on the boundary of our world; Rackham's faeries also live beneath the trees, among their roots, as seen in *Faerie Folk*, the

Fig. 2 'The Fairy Queen's Messenger',
World of Faerie (2007). Credit: Brian Froud.
Fig. 3 'Indi, the Indecision Faery', *Bad
Faeries* (1998). Credit: Brian Froud.
Fig. 4 'The Gloominous Doom', *Bad
Faeries* (1998). Credit: Brian Froud.
Fig. 5 'A Damp Fairy', *Lady Cottington's
Fairy Album* (2002). Credit: Brian Froud.
Fig. 6 'Flying Faery'. Credit: Wendy Froud.

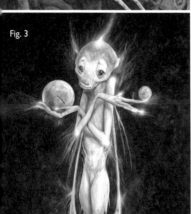

Fig. 6

frontispiece of *Imagina* (1914) by Julia Ellsworth Ford, and *Peter Pan in Kensington Gardens* (1906); even from an urban park they observe us unseen. Under the auspices of George Cruikshank and Charles Robinson, goblins developed as a genre in their own right: drawing on the Brothers Grimm, Cruikshank's *Grimm's Goblins* appeared in 1876, while Robinson's *Book of Goblins, a collection of folk-lore and fairy tales* was published in 1934. In these works goblins and humans often interact; they are co-existent inhabitants of 'long ago, and far away'. Froud's creatures exist in a world of their own, in the 'Otherworld of Faery'.[14] This is not the Land of Once Upon a Time; Froud's 'real' faerie-land is imbued with Power, 'magical power, incomprehensible to humans, and hence, inimical'; faeries are 'alien creatures with values and ethics far removed from mankind'.[15] We are lured into this world by its mystery and strange beauty but we must enter with caution. Faeries do not welcome unbidden intrusions; the dangers are real.

Moreover, faeries envy mortals and all too often covet our belongings and even our children. Human babies are needed to inject fresh blood into the race; in 'Labyrinth' (1986) Sarah accidentally wishes her baby half-brother, Toby, away to the Goblin King Jareth; if Sarah does not complete Jareth's Labyrinth in thirteen hours she will lose him to the Goblin King. With the role of Jareth played by David Bowie, and Toby actually the Froud's own son, 'Labyrinth' has achieved cult status.

Froud sets out to define, through line and colour, the Otherworld of Faery, a 'world of dark enchantments, of captivating beauty, of enormous ugliness, of callous superficiality, of humour, mischief, joy and inspiration'.[16] Capturing the nature of faerie is a difficult task, as Froud admits, as 'they are not normally visible and are elusive, mutable, delight in being "tricksy" and will not sit for long'.[17] Froud attempts to 'classify' the Denizens of Faerie by drawing on legends, myths, folklore and poems. Apparently there are good and bad faeries, although good and bad coexist in all faerie creatures. Utilising the elements, faeries are divided into earth (gnomes, brownies, and kobolds), water (nixies, lamias and undines), fire (salamanders, daemons, and fire drakes) and air (sylphs, peries, and all winged faeries).[18] But in addition to traditional faeries, taken from Anglo-Saxon, Welsh and Irish folklore, Froud creates his own classifications that appeal to modern sensibilities as well as children. The Bad Hair Day Faery tangles our hair during the night. The Foot Fungus Faery causes athlete's foot or ringworm, 'a fungal faery ring, personalised in miniature'.[19] Another exasperating faery is the Pen Stealer, while the Fee Lion, who embodies a 'slight accusation', mimics a cat, the witch's favourite familiar, and is the source of faint scratching in the early hours or mysterious midnight mewings. Traditionally he is heard inside cupboards and bedrooms – always on the other side of doors; he is to blame when keys are locked in a car! The Fee Lion is the accusing voice in your head, as you fall asleep, compelling you to do all those little chores – feed the cat, clean the oven or write a thank-you note. These are clearly contemporary *lares*, the domestic spirits beloved of the Romans, who have adapted to our ways. Other Froud creations reflect modern-day angst: Indi, the Indecision Faery, is a troublesome creature who can pop up anywhere; he's the one who won't let you make up your mind, forever weighing up the pros and cons (Fig. 3). We have all encountered The Gloominous Doom, who despairs and moans 'I can't do it'; he holds the 'globe of clear thinking' unexamined behind him. The globe contains all his lost hopes, turned heavy with his pessimism. 'It's too late now', he sighs wearily, 'It's all behind me now.'[20] (Fig. 4)

The Lady Cottington series humorously exploits the Cottingley Fairies by alleging that fairies can be pressed like flowers, as well as captured in photographs.[21] The Cottingley Fairies caused a sensation in 1917; Elsie Wright and Frances Griffiths claimed not only to have seen fairies but also to have photographed them. Sir Arthur Conan Doyle, still mourning the death of his son in the Great War and in the grip of spiritualism, believed them. Convinced by the photographs, Doyle published *The Coming of the Fairies* (1922). In 1981 Elsie and Frances admitted to faking all but one of the photographs but insisted they really had seen fairies.[22]

Rather than utilising photography, Lady Angelica Cottington, the 'infamous fairy squasher', captured images of fairies by pressing them in an album: 'messy but effective. I am perfecting my technique. One has to be very quick indeed, then a firm squeeze. One learns in time to ignore the little cries.'[23] (Fig. 5) In the third book in the series, *Lady Cottington's Fairy Album* (2002), Froud assures us that the Royal Society for the Prevention of Cruelty to Fairies has verified that no fairies were killed or injured in the making of the book. Rather, the images are psychic imprints, the fairies themselves flying away unseen and unharmed.

In the same book it is revealed that Angelica had an older sister, Euphemia, who captured her fairies photographically using a variety of novel techniques. Froud admits that Euphemia's photographs, like those taken by Elsie and Frances, initially appear to be forgeries based on paper cut-outs. But the later images and text are 'deeply convincing and appear ... to describe genuine fairy contact for the first time'.[24] Apparently Euphemia has truly encountered the faeries; driven by her desire to escape the strictures of Victorian society, Euphemia is lured into the woods by the faeries, where her passionate, natural, self is revealed. Like Christina Rossetti's Laura in *Goblin Market* (1862), Euphemia tastes the fairy fruit and is inevitably seduced by the 'gardener's boy'; her early death is attributed to her running off with the fairies. But a dark secret is revealed at the close of the book; Euphemia is Angelica's mother. This fairy child clearly needs to stay away from the woods!

The idea of capturing their image or being able to see faeries clearly fascinates Froud; *How to see Faeries* (2011), with John Matthews, uses paper mechanics – pop-ups, window insets, cut-outs and reflective mirrors – to enable us to see into the world of faerie. *The Faeries' Oracle* (2000), with Jessica Macbeth, offers us another way into faerie through symbols of the alchemical processes of transformation and sacred geometry; this divination set, following the tradition of tarot, numbers sixty-six cards featuring goblins, pixies, boggarts, and other faery folk first encountered in *Good Faeries/Bad Faeries*. By learning how to read the cards, the initiate will be able to connect with the faeries by opening a portal to their world. *The Heart of Faerie Oracle* (2010) is a reworking of the tarot card theme, this time in collaboration with Wendy, who provides much of the accompanying text.

Wendy's role in creating the *World of Froud* should not be underestimated; Jim Henson employed this talented model/doll maker from Detroit to sculpt the lead characters for 'The Dark Crystal', the Gelfings Jen and Kira. Wendy's fabrication brought Brian's creatures into three-dimensional life; named after *Peter Pan's* Wendy, she is Brian's acknowledged 'faerie woman' Muse, a Divine Feminine: 'Dear Reader, I married one – finest of all Faerie – Wendy Froud. Enchantress, inspirer, and faerie muse'.[25] The spirit of Wendy's model work is closely akin to Brian's vision: 'I like to think of the figures I make as companions for a personal journey. I try to fill each one with healing energy that responds to the person who owns it, and conversely, I hope that the person who owns it will respond with a true heart connection' (Fig. 6).[26] The Frouds have forged their Otherworld in tandem:

> I was introduced to Brian's work by Jim Henson on the day
> I was hired to work on a new project called The Dark Crystal …
> I had never before seen fantasy painting and illustration that
> touched me as Brian's did. I grew up loving Arthur Rackham's
> illustrations, but these had a life and immediacy to them that
> went far beyond illustration … They were waiting to be released
> from the page so that they could inhabit this world as fully and
> immediately as their own. Ours is a marriage of heart and art.
> It has remained one of my greatest pleasures to sculpt from
> Brian's designs and see these creatures take form in front of us
> in all their mischievous glory.[27]

Their son Toby, having played the role of the stolen baby in 'Labyrinth', has also entered the world of Froud; he is currently working at Laika Animation Studios in Portland, Oregon, on the fabrication of puppets for the stop-motion film 'ParaNorman'. Perhaps, like Lady Angelica, being a faerie child, he could not avoid his fate: 'growing up in a home with two artists naturally encouraged me to follow their steps … Seeing the creativity and passion that drives my parents has always been an inspiration to me.'[28] The Frouds latest venture is *Brian Froud's Trolls* (2012), which explores troll culture, revealing their home life, their outlook and even their philosophical thoughts through folklore, mythology and archaeology. With creatures echoing his conceptual design work for 'The Dark Crystal', it is hoped the much anticipated sequel will be put into production sooner rather than later.

. . . .

Anne Anderson

References

1. Cheryl Henson, 'Foreword', *Visions for Film and Faerie, exhibition and sale of original works Brian-Wendy-Toby Froud*, Animazing Gallery, SoHo, NYC, December 2011.

2. Ari Berk, 'Foreword', *Brian Froud's World of Faerie*, San Rafael, CA: Insight Editions, 2007, p.6.

3. *Visions for Film and Faerie*, p.33.

4. Heidi Leigh, 'Preface', *Visions for Film and Faerie, exhibition and sale of original works Brian-Wendy-Toby Froud*, Animazing Gallery, SoHo, NYC, December 2011, p.i.

5. Fred Hauptfuhrer, 'For Artists Alan Lee & Brian Froud, Life Is a Faerie Tale Come True', *People Magazine*, Vol. 11, No. 11, 19 March 1979, p.126.

6. *Ibid.*

7. Leigh, 'Brian Froud is the most important faerie artist of our time', *Visions for Film and Faerie, exhibition and sale of original works Brian-Wendy-Toby Froud*, Animazing Gallery, SoHo, NYC, December 2011.

8. Anne Anderson and Graham Ovenden, *The Truth About Faeries from A Midsummer Night's Dream to The Lord of the Rings*, exhibition catalogue, Southampton City Art Gallery, 2009, p.104.

9. Brian Froud, 'Welcome', *The Secret Sketchbooks of Brian Froud*, Los Angeles: Imaginosis, 2006.

10. Froud, *Brian Froud's World of Faerie*, p.19.

11. *The Windmill: Stories, Essays, Poems & Pictures by Authors and Artists whose Works are published at the Sign of the Windmill*, 1923.

12. 'The Briar Wood', 'The Council Chamber', 'The Garden Court' and 'The Rose Bower'.

13. Froud, *Brian Froud's World of Faerie*, p.74.

14. Froud, *The Secret Sketchbooks of Brian Froud*, p.2.

15. Betty Ballantine, 'Foreword', *Faeries Described and Illustrated by Brian Froud and Alan Lee*, New York, Toronto and London: Peacock Press/Bantum Books, 1978, p.3.

16. *Ibid.*

17. Froud, *The Secret Sketchbooks of Brian Froud*, p.2.

18. Brian Froud, 'Introduction', *Good Faeries/Bad Faeries*, New York: Simon and Schuster Editions, 1998, p.9.

19. Froud, *Bad Faeries*.

20. Froud, *Bad Faeries*.

21. Brian Froud and Terry Jones, *Lady Cottington's Pressed Fairy Book*, 1994, and *Lady Cottington's Pressed Fairy Journal*, London: Pavilion Books, 1996; *Quentin Cottington's Journal of Faery Research: Strange Stains and Mysterious Smells* (1996); *Lady Cottington's Fairy Album*, New York: Harry Abrams, 2002.

22. Geoffrey Crawley, 'The Astonishing Affair of the Cottingley Fairies', *British Journal of Photography*, 1882-3, parts 1-10.

23. Froud, *Lady Cottington's Fairy Album*.

24. Froud, *Lady Cottington's Fairy Album*, p.1.

25. Froud, *Brian Froud's World of Faerie*, p.84.

26. Leigh, *Visions for Film and Faerie*, p.91.

27. *The Art of Wendy Froud*, Los Angeles: Imaginois, 2006, p.43.

28. Leigh, *Visions for Film and Faerie*, p.101.

Trolls

By Brian & Wendy Froud. Published by Abrams Books

Publication Date: September 2012, Price: £21.99, ISBN: 9781419704383

Not since Brian's conceptual design work with Jim Henson on the classic films, 'The Dark Crystal' and 'Labyrinth', has Brian created a faerie world with such imagination, dimension, depth and detail. *Trolls* is a large format "world book" that explores trolls and troll culture in a dynamic merging of pictures and words that brings their world vividly alive. *Trolls* reveals the past, present and future of these magical creatures through images, tales, mythology and archaeology. *Trolls* presents strong, individual, heroic characters and reveals troll philosophy and wisdom with contemporary relevance. Most importantly, *Trolls* is bound together with a compelling narrative: a central story that affirms that trolls are real, have lived and are living now.

Trolls features new and classic 2D and 3D work by both Brian and Wendy that are woven together with troll "artefacts", symbols and the natural world to create a fascinating revelation of their world. Brian's images are deeply immersive, even cinematic at times; *Trolls* draws the viewer into the texture of the world and its stories of characters born of lichened rocks, twisted trees, rainbowed waterfalls and shadowy thickets.

Author/Artist

Brian Froud has created some of the most respected and highly acknowledged mythic artwork of our time. His work has been the inspiration for such films as 'The Dark Crystal' and 'Labyrinth' (both with Jim Henson's Creature Shop). He has won numerous awards, including an Award for Best Original Artwork. Wendy Froud is a doll-artist, sculptor and puppet-maker, best known for her work creating creatures for the Jim Henson films 'The Dark Crystal' and 'Labyrinth' as well as work on the Star Wars films including being the fabricator of Yoda.

Brian and Wendy
Froud, *Brian
Froud's Trolls.*

An interview with Brian Froud

Heather Robbins

F or over 35 years, Brian Froud has been an internationally renowned and bestselling faerie artist and an authority on faeries and faerie lore. His international best-selling book, *Faeries*, with fantasy illustrator Alan Lee, is a modern classic of art and British fairy folklore, while his cult hit movies with Jim Henson, 'The Dark Crystal' and 'Labyrinth', set new standards for design, puppeteering and animatronics. With over eight million books sold to date, Brian's international bestsellers include the *Lady Cottington's Pressed Fairy Album* series with Monty Python's Terry Jones and Prof. Ari Berk, *Good Faeries/Bad Faeries* and the *Faeries Oracle*, as well as collaborations with Prof. Ari Berk on *Goblins!*, the *Runes of Elfland* and *Brian Froud's World of Faerie*. Two festival events, Faerieworlds and FaerieCon, are held in his honour and attract over 30,000 guests each year. Brian lives in Devon, England, with his wife, internationally acclaimed doll maker Wendy Froud. Their latest book, *Trolls*, is available now. Sussex Centre assistant Heather Robbins interviewed him on his work, his plans for the future and, of course, *Trolls*.

Brian, your work always appears to stay close to the traditions of fairy folklore. What percentage of your working time is taken up with researching fairy folklore as opposed to painting and sketching, or are the two activities closely bound up in one continuous process?

I hardly ever read novels but I do lots of research reading, the more obscure, the better, usually the book at the bottom of a tottering pile in my studio – unfortunately I never remember anything, but it does have a way of percolating through and emerging in my art, so it must all be in there somewhere.

Where do you go or what resources do you use for your research? Is there a particular book that's falling apart from over-use as inspiration?

Over the years I have collected a large library of research books – in fact they are taking over most of my studio at this point. I do have books I return to more often than most – anything by John Matthews but especially **The Western Way,** *by Caitlin and John Matthews.*

I have not had chance to see *Trolls* yet, but I've read that it includes troll 'artefacts' and an exploration of 'troll culture' through their tales, mythology, and archaeology. Can you explain more?

These are local trolls (Dartmoor) — not the Nordic trolls that people are most familiar with. Wendy and I have tried to give the reader a glimpse into their world by presenting not only images of the trolls themselves but using photographs of their symbolic, ritual and everyday objects with explanations as well as recording their tales and tale fragments.

Aren't trolls just grumpy creatures living under bridges? Did you uncover any folklore that suggested otherwise?

Yes — we suggest that trolls, for the most part, are not lurking under bridges but supporting the structure of the bridge and are indeed sometimes the bridges themselves, connecting our world with an inner world. Of course, there ARE those few really bad trolls that do just lurk, but they are in the minority.

Your book *Faeries* struck such a chord because it felt like the first illustrated book on fairies in a long time that had depicted them as tricksy, grown-up, even dangerous. Do you hope that *Trolls* will change the general opinion of trolls in the same way?

Yes! We hope so. We felt that trolls had had a bad press for years and that it was time to redress the balance.

Did your experience of painting trolls differ from your experiences of previous books with fairies and goblins? Did trolls offer new challenges or lessons?

The challenge was to have continuity between the new work and the paintings, of which there are quite a few in this book, that I painted over thirty years ago — however it was mainly pretty easy because trolls insisted on looking the way they look.

As a student of Celtic and world mythology, do you think the old myths are still relevant in modern times? Or are they more to be used as a romantic escape and a source of inspiration?

They always will be relevant because they aren't about a romantic past but are an expression of the land itself. The tales and the songs are embedded in the landscape and speak to us now as strongly as they ever did.

The fairy-tale landscape of Dartmoor, your home, and its rich folklore are very evident in your work and have inspired many other artists and writers. Do you think your art would be very different (or even impossible) if you lived elsewhere?

Not impossible but it would not be as true or strong if I lived elsewhere.

The variety of media used in your artwork, the glowing earthy colours, and the emotive expressions given to each fairy creature, are a very potent combination and create, I think it can be fairly said, an inimitable style. I read that a book of Arthur Rackham's work inspired you at art college – are there any other artists whom you particularly admire?

Obviously John Bauer, the Pre-Raphaelites, the northern European Renaissance artists, Durer, Brueghel and Bosch.

Copies of your books, especially *Faeries*, are invariably much treasured and well-worn. What quality is it that allows you to create artwork with such a powerful effect on people, and which continues to top the bestsellers' list for over 35 years?

I think it's because the work is truthful and heartfelt and there is a quality about the work that defies ordinary explanation. I am grateful to have been a part of this.

May we ask, as we ask everyone at some point, what your favourite fairy tale was when you were a child?

It was 'The Tinderbox' (I think that's the title but I'm not certain) by Hans Christian Anderson – the one with the dog with the eyes as big as saucers. It was partly the story and partly the illustration that went with it in the book I had – I don't remember who the illustrator was – it wasn't anyone well known.

I heard that while you usually prefer to create the picture and allow the text to form later, you might one day be tempted to illustrate Mervyn Peake's *Gormenghast*. We're big fans of Mervyn Peake here at the Sussex Centre – in fact, Prof. Bill Gray is currently working with Peter Winnington on a book of last year's Peake conference that includes many of Peake's own illustrations. Do you think your own edition of *Gormenghast* is likely to happen or are there too many projects going on at the moment for you to seriously consider it?

I fell in love with his dark world years ago when I was young, but I really feel that I want to explore my own worlds, dark and otherwise.

. . . .

Interview by Heather Robbins

Alan Lee,
'Hunting Twyth',
The Mabinogion.

Gwyn ap Nudd: Transfigurations of a character on the way from medieval literature to neo-pagan beliefs

Angelika H. Rüdiger

A ny character originating in folk tradition and used for a long time in poetry, fiction and art is subject to a gradual transfiguration of its features due to interplay between oral tradition and written sources, between folklore and literature, between creative writing and compiling scholarly opinion and research results. This interplay may result in changes and transfigurations of the 'original' meaning and characteristics, or – more correctly – to the meaning and characteristics this character had at a certain point in time that is chosen as a reference point.

This paper will present a concise summary of the main transfigurations which Gwyn ap Nudd (Foster 1953; Bartrum 1993), a supernatural character from Welsh tradition, also known as King of the Fairies, *Brenin y Tylwyth Teg*, has been subjected to. It covers the time from his first appearance in medieval literature to the present and his meaning within neo-pagan beliefs. The objective is to provide a guide into this vast matter rather than an in-depth discussion of the various items. The most important catalysts in a long-standing development will be highlighted.

Thus, this paper will be structured according to the chronology of the evidence. It will begin with the introduction of Gwyn ap Nudd as presented by the medieval and early modern sources, followed by some considerations of his role in Welsh folklore. The features newly attributed to him during the time of Romanticism will be briefly covered, followed by an assessment of the ideas Sir John Rhys developed about Gwyn which are virtually the key to understanding the image of this character within today's neo-pagan beliefs. It will continue by showing the role Gwyn was assigned in the works of Robert Graves and Gerald Gardner, who each had a tremendous influence on the neo-pagan reception of Gwyn. The closing section will summarise the consequences of ideas developed by Rhys, Graves and Gardner for the modern neo-pagan image and function of Gwyn ap Nudd.

Medieval and early modern sources

Poem XXXIV of the *Black Book of Carmarthen*

Gwyn ap Nudd is a fictional character, who appeared for the first time in poem XXXIV of the *Black Book of Carmarthen* (Jarman and Jones 1982). The manuscript dates back to the middle of the 13th century (Jarman 1985; Huws 2000; Dengholm 1954), but the poem was presumably written at the end of the 11th century, as linguistic evidence shows (Rowland 1990). This text is central for the analysis of the transfigurations Gwyn was subjected to by scholars in the 19th century. Therefore, I will present the text of the *Black Book* following the edition of Jarman (Jarman and Jones 1982) together with a translation.

The dialogue of Gwyn ap Nudd and Gwyddno Garanhir

1.   *Tarv trin anvidin blaut*
    arbenic llu llid anhaut
    Dinam eiroes am oes naut.

    Bull of battle, fierce, terrible,
    Ruler of a host, unpleasant in wrath,
    Of perfect trust, I ask you for protection.

2.   *Y gan gur gurt y kinnit.*
    arbennic llv llidowit.
    ath vit naut canys erchit.

    From a hero of valiant supremacy,
    Ruler of a host, lord of wrath,
    You get protection because you seek it.

3.   *Can is naut im a rotit.*
    mor verth yth ogyuechit.
    guaur llv py dv pan doit.

    Since you give me so fine protection
    I ask you,
    Hero of a host, where do you come from?

4.   *Ban deuaw o kad a chiminad maur*
    ac aessaur in aghad
    briuint penaur peleidrad.

    I come from a battle and great slaughter,
    Shield in hand,
    Pushing of spears bruised heads.

5.   *Ath kiuarchaw hvyscun gur.*
    ae iscuid in aghen.
    pebirgur pan iv dy echen.

    I greet you steadfast hero
    With shield in hand.
    Brave warrior what is your descent?

6.   *Caringrun wi march kad trablunt.*
    hud im gelwir e guin mab nud.
    gorterch creurdilad merch lut.

    Round-hoofed is my horse, agitation of battle,
    Thus I am called Gwyn ap Nudd,
    The lover of Creiddylad merch Ludd.

7. Can is ti guin gur kiwir.
   racod ny ryimgelir
   Minnev guitnev garanhir.

   Because you are Gwyn, an upright hero,
   From you I do not conceal
   I am Gwyddno Garanhir.

8. Nim gad e gan kyulauaret a thi.
   urth i fruin yd wet.
   dywris im trum tawuy a net.

   The white horse does not allow me
   conversation with you
   Because it leads with the bridle
   It hastens away to the ridge of Tawe and Nedd.

9. Nid y tawue nessaw a lawaraw urthid.
   namvin y tawue eithaw.
   Erir mor terruin treiaw.

   I do not speak of the nearest Tawe
   But of the farthest Tawe.
   Eagle of the fierce sea, I will retreat.

10. Yscithreid vy modruy eur kywruy cann.
    y gan wy auarvy.
    gueleis aer rac kaer wantvy.

    Engraved is my ring, the white horse has a
    golden saddle
    Because of my vanity
    I saw a battle before Caer Fandwy.

11. Rac mantvy llv a weleis
    aessaur brihuid. torrhid eis.
    mygedaul. kein a dygei treis.

    Before Mandwy I saw a host,
    Shields broken, ribs (spears) broken,
    The honourable and beautiful waged war.

12. Gwin ab nut but. bitinaur.
    kint y sirthei kadoet rac carnetaur dy ueirch
    no bruyn briw y laur.

    Gwyn benefit of the hosts,
    Sooner armies would fall before the hooves of
    your horse
    than rushes broken to the ground.

13. Ys tec vy ki ac is trun.
    Ac yss ew. orev or cvn.
    Dormarch oet hunnv a fv y maelgun.

    Beautiful is my dog and fine,
    he is the best of dogs.
    Dormarch was that one that belonged to
    Maelgwn.

14. Dormach truinrut ba ssillit arnaw
    caniss amgiffredit.
    dy gruidir ar wibir winit.

    Dormarch of the ruddy nose at what are you
    looking.
    Since I cannot understand
    Your wandering on the sky mountains.

15 *Mi a wum in y lle llas guendolev.*　　I have been at the place of death of Gwenddoleu
　　mab keidav colowin kertev.　　Son of Ceidio, supporter of poetry
　　ban ryerhint brein ar crev.　　When ravens screamed over blood.

16 *Mi a wum in lle llas bran*　　I have been at the place of Bran's death,
　　mab ywerit clod lydan.　　Son of Ywerydd of wide praise.
　　ban ryerint brein garthan.　　When carrion crows screamed.

17 *Mi a wum lle llas llachev*　　I have been where Llacheu died,
　　mab arthur uthir ig kertev.　　Son of Arthur marvelous in songs
　　ban ryreint brein ar crev.　　When ravens scream over blood.

18 *Mi a wum lle llas meuric*　　I have been in the place of the death of Meurig
　　Mab kareian clod edmic.　　Son of Careian of honorable praises,
　　ban ryreeint brein ar cic.　　When ravens screamed over flesh.

19 *Ny buum lle llas gwallauc*　　I have not been where Gwallawg died
　　mab goholheth teithiauc　　Son of a lawful prince,
　　attwod lloegir mab lleynnac　　The trouble for England, son of Lleennawg.

20 *Mi a wum lle llas milvir pridein.*　　I have been where the soldiers of Britain died
　　or duyrein ir goglet.　　From the east to the north.
　　Mi. wi. wiw. vintev. y. bet.　　I am, they [are] in the grave.

21 *Mi a wum lle llas milguir bridein*　　I have been where the soldiers of Britain died
　　or duyrein ir dehev.　　From the east to the south
　　Mi. wi. wiv. vintev y aghev.　　I am, they [are] in death (transl. A.R.).

Stanzas 1, 3, 5, 7, 12 and 14 are attributed to Gwyddno Garanhir and 2, 4, 6, 8-11, 13, 15-21 to Gwyn ap Nudd. The poem of the *Black Book of Carmarthen* depicts Gwyn as a hunter and warrior, a leader of a host and a supernatural character; the latter is accomplished by Gwyn's mentioning of Caer Fandwy, an otherworldly fortress which seems to be located in Annwn according to the poem *Preiddeu Annwn* (The Spoils of Annwn). This poem is found in *Llyfr Taliesin* (Book of Taliesin), dating back to the 14th century (Higley 2012). The Welsh noun 'Annwn' denotes a realm beyond the world of men, literally the 'Non-World'. It is described as a beautiful land in 'The First Branch of the Mabinogi', and as a consequence has to be regarded as the Welsh equivalent to the Irish 'Otherworld'. However, in the course of time this expression has gradually undergone a change of meaning, so that it could be used in modern times as equivalent to the term 'uffern', 'hell', in a Christian sense (GPC; Koch 2006).

Gwyn is equipped with all the epithets and attributes of the formidable hero familiar from the contemporary saga poetry (Jarman 1967) and from the heroic poetry of Aneirin, *Y Gododdin* (Williams 1970; Evans 1908). Gwyn is a hero, a terrible 'bull of battle', and he is noted for his reverence for a lady, as he introduces himself as lover of Creiddylad. He appears as a splendid knight on a white horse with a golden saddle and a precious ring.

The heroes of the contemporary and earlier poetry are described with equivalent terms. The metaphor 'bull of battle' is used quite frequently. It can be found for example in the poem *Enwev meibion llywarch hen* (Llywarch Hen's sons' names) (Rowland 1990). The hero Eithinyn is entitled 'bull of combat' in the poem *Y Gododdin*, and the Welsh Triads, *Trioedd Ynys Prydein*, list 'three Bull-protectors of the island of Britain', the hero Gwenddoleu, lamented by Gwyn ap Nudd, being one of them, and 'three bull-chieftains of the island of Britain' (Bromwich 1961, 7). A hero was expected to be terrible in battle. In *Y Gododdin* Madog is described as follows: 'he showed no mercy to those whom he pursued/ He did not withdraw from battle until blood flowed'; Isag is described as 'unwavering in his ferocity'. Owain ap Urien is called 'reaper of enemies' in his death song. But on the other hand a hero who cuts down 'enemies like rushes' could well be 'breathless before a maiden', like Madog in the poem *Y Gododdin*. The 'swan-coloured horses' (*Y Gododdin*) as well as the 'shining mail-shirts and swords' (*ibid*.; Jarman 1967), and the 'spurs of gold' like those of Gwen in the *Llywarch hen* poems (Rowland 1990), complete the image of the formidable hero. Thus, Gwyn riding his white horse, with his golden saddle and precious ring, fits perfectly into this image of the ideal knight and hero.

It is obvious that the choice of metaphors and epithets relates the poem about Gwyn to the heroic world of *Y Gododdin* described by Aneirin, who tells in his poem about a host of warriors and heroes of the Old North, *Yr Hen Ogledd* – a region which comprised the south of Scotland and the north of England.

However, this relationship between poem XXXIV of the *Black Book of Carmarthen* and the Old North is not only established by drafting the image of Gwyn ap Nudd in a way which has been applied to the heroes of this region before, but also by the content of the poem. Gwyn ap Nudd is associated with the men of the Old North, especially with a group of warriors and princes who were in conflict with the kin and the patrons of Cynderyn Garthwys (St Kentigern) (Rowland 1990; Bartrum 1993). Gwyn ap Nudd has been present at the battles in which they lost their lives, and it is their death which Gwyn is lamenting.

Culwch ac Olwen

The earliest prose text mentioning Gwyn is the tale *Culwch ac Olwen* found in the *White Book of Rhydderch* (Evans 1907; Davies 2007). This text is part of the 11 vernacular tales which are sometimes referred to collectively as the *Mabinogi* or *Mabinogion*. The present redaction of the text is assumed to date back to 1100 A.D. (Foster 1953).

The tale *Culhwch ac Olwen* tells how Culhwch was obliged to hunt the monster boar Twrch Trwyth in order to obtain the comb and the shears that lay between its ears, as the father of his beloved Olwen, the giant Ysbaddaden, wanted to have them before he would give his daughter Olwen to Culhwch. Culhwch is aided by King Arthur and all his court to cope with this and other difficult tasks. The setting of the story strongly reminds one of the Irish tales, especially the deeds of the Tuatha de Danann or the Finn-cycle. The king and his heroes clearly show supernatural traits. The hunt of a monster boar and the courting of a lady of non-human lineage, the daughter of the giant Ysbaddaden, Olwen, are the key issues of this story.

It is notable that this story about an adventure of Arthur and his heroes pre-dates Geoffrey of Monmouth, whose work laid the foundations of the vast literature on Arthurian romance all over Europe. Actually *Culhwch ac Olwen* is the earliest Arthurian tale in any language (Gantz 1976).

For a successful boar hunt Arthur's host of excellent heroes must be joined by Gwyn ap Nudd, who needs the famous sea-going horse Du y Moroedd, 'Black of the Seas' (Bromwich 1961, 113-14) to take part in this hunting company. The redactor tells us: '*Ny heli[r] Twrch Trwyth nes kaffel Guynn mab Nudd ar dodes Duw aryal dieul Annwuyn yndaw rac rewinnyaw y bressen. Ny hebcorir ef odyno.*' (Bromwich and Evans 1997, 26-7): 'Twrch Trwyth is not hunted until one gets Gwyn ap Nudd in whom God put the spirit of the devils of Annwn lest the world would be destroyed. He cannot be spared from there.' Thus, Gwyn is presented as lord over a tribe of demonic spirits and being also filled with demonic powers. Gwyn's leaving Annwn would endanger the very existence of the world.

Yet, despite all this, Gwyn joins the hunting company. This is the story according to the *White Book*. The *Red Book*, however, enters him as a member of Arthur's court, which is an anachronism according to the further plot of the story, but need not be discussed in the context of this essay.

In the course of events, Gwyn is introduced as the lover of Creiddylad in that he has actually taken her away from Gwythyr ap Greidawl, with whom the girl went. But before Gwythyr could enjoy the pleasures of being her lover or husband, Gwyn abducted Creiddylad and fought against the host which Gwythyr had gathered in order to win back the lady from his rival. In this battle Gwyn was victorious, took captives, a certain Greid ap Eri among them, and treated the warriors who had dared to challenge him most cruelly.

Arthur, however, obviously has the authority to make peace between the rivals for Creiddylad's love. He sentences them to fight every 1st May for the girl, who was to stay undisturbed by either party in the house of her father. The yearly fighting was to end no sooner than the world would end. The winner on the Day of Judgment could then keep the girl.

Further on in the story, Arthur always relies on Gwyn's advice when things become really difficult. Thus Gwyn's advice is needed for the hunt of Twrch Trwyth and when the blood of the Black Hag has to be obtained.

The redactor of the *Culhwch ac Olwen* tale depicts Gwyn as a hunter-warrior with magical powers, but by saying that 'God put the spirit of the devils of Annwn [in him] lest the world would be destroyed', he classifies the inhabitants of Annwn as 'devils'. This sentence shows the Christian bias of the redactor (Foster 1953), but it also characterises Gwyn as the antagonist of 'this world', i.e. the world of men, as he is equipped with powers threatening this world.

All this dovetails with the fact that *Culhwch ac Olwen* is not only the source of Gwyn's and Gwythyr's yearly combat for Creiddylad. Moreover, the tale shows most clearly of all sources a similarity of Gwyn to Finn mac Umaill (aka Finn McCool) in that Gwyn is a character belonging to the 'World of the Outlaw' in the sense Josph Nagy uses this term (Nagy 1985; Nagy 1987).

Gwyn's being the Welsh equivalent to Finn mac Umaill has long been suggested based on the etymology of the names 'Finn' and 'Gwyn' ('white, fair, blessed') and a comparable ancestry when considering the Welsh 'Nudd' and the Irish 'Nuada' as equivalent characters (Murphy 1953; Foster 1953; Chadwick 1931). Actually, a careful analysis of the tale *Culwch ac Olwen* suggests that the similarities between Finn and Gwyn go beyond this.

Gerard Murphy identifies one of the oldest motifs connected with Finn as his fight against a 'malevolent burner', often discernible in the tales by a fire-related name of the latter (Murphy 1953). Joseph Nagy highlights the importance of Finn being trained and educated by druid-warrior women in the wilderness (*dá benfénnidi; bendruí*). He also draws attention to the first right of the Fenians, the warriors led by Finn mac Umaill, to any girl who should be given into marriage. Moreover, Joseph Nagy highlights the fact that the Fenian leader's unsocial love affairs often represent a destabilising element for society. He also shows convincingly that the actual objective of the Fiana was to mediate passage-rites exceeding all common experience (Nagy 1985).

All those elements are found in Gwyn in the tale *Culhwch ac Olwen*. His chief foe Gwythyr ap Greidawl bears a name related to 'heat, passion' – '*greid*' – in its patronym, as is the name of another of Gwyn's foes, of Greid ap Eri. Gwyn takes Creiddylad shortly before her transition from a maiden to a wife, and the eternal yearly combat for her takes place at the transition of winter to summer, at the calends of May (*Calan Mai*). The episode in which Arthur calls Gwyn and Gwythyr because he wants to ask them for advice on how to deal with the witches (*Y Gwiddonod*) could well be understood as a motif drawing on some lost tradition in which both Gwyn and Gwythyr are especially familiar with the ways of those wild warrior women.

All those elements reinforce the suggestion that Gwyn ap Nudd belongs to the 'World of the Outlaw', the world outside the well-ordered society of man, which is needed at times to protect the world against demonic forces, like the boar Twrch Trwyth, but at the same time induces a destabilising element for the order in the realm of men.

The poetry of the Poets of the Gentry

Furthermore, Gwyn ap Nudd is mentioned in various poems by the so-called poets of the gentry, the most famous being Dafydd ap Gwilym, but also by Wiliam Llyn, Huw Machno, Rhisiart Phylip, Rhisiart Cynwal and Gruffudd Hiraethog (Roberts 1980/1).

In accordance with the observation that Gwyn ap Nudd is shown as a representative of the 'World of the Outlaw', a world which lies beyond the ploughed and tilled fields, the poets of the gentry (Johnston 1999; Roberts 1980/1) show Gwyn as a representative of wild nature and the world outside the cultivated world of human society, the wilderness, murky times and unpleasant places. It is Dafydd ap Gwilym who knows that Gwyn ap Nudd can 'take people'. Gruffudd Hiraethog for his part brings Gwyn ap Nudd into connection with the *Cwn Annwn*, the Dogs of Annwn (Jones 1979), thus relating him to the motif-complex of the Spectral Hunt (Roberts 1980/1).

A fragment of Dafydd ap Gwilym's famous poem *Y Niwl* illustrates how Gwyn and Annwn are used as reference points to describe the oppressive mist:

Fragment of 'Y Niwl '(DAG)

Codarmur cawad ormes,	*coat of armour of an oppressive shower,*
Twyllai wyr, tywyll o wedd,	*it would deceive men, dark appearance,*
Toron gwrddonig tiredd,	*shaggy cloak of the lands,*
Tyrau uchel eu helynt	*towers of Gwyn's tribe*
Tylwyth Gwyn, talaith y gwynt,	*travelling on high, headdress of the wind,*
Tir a gudd ei ddeurudd ddygn,	*its grim cheeks hide the land,*
Torsed yn cuddio teirsygn,	*a blanket covering three signs of the Zodiac,*
Tywyllwg, un tew allardd,	*darkness, a thick unlovely one,*
Delli byd i dwyllo bardd,	*blindness of the world to deceive a poet,*
Llydanwe gombr gosombraff,	*broad web of thick deceptive cambric,*
Ar lled y'i rhodded fal rhaff,	*it was spread out like a rope,*
Gwe adrgop, Ffrengigsiop ffrwyth,	*a spider's web, like wares of a French shop,*
Gwan dalar Gwyn a'i dylwyth,	*flaccid headland of Gwyn and his tribe,*
Mwg brych yn fynych a fydd,	*speckled smoke which gets everywhere,*
Mogodarth cylch meigoedydd,	*steam around small trees,*
Anadl arth lle cyfarth cwn,	*bear's breath where dogs bark,*
Ennaint gwrachïod Annwn,	*ointment of the witches of Annwn,*
Gochwith megis gwlith y gwlych,	*it wets stealthily like dew,*
Habrsiwn tir anehwybrsych. […]	*damp opaque habergeon of the land.[…]*

Two religious texts deal with Gwyn ap Nudd as well: the *Life of St Collen* (*Buchedd Collen*) and a fragment in a text called *Speculum Christiani* (Roberts 1980/1).

Buchedd Collen

The earliest version of *Buchedd Collen*, the life (*vita*) of St Collen, dates back to 1536 (BC; Henken 1987; Henken 1991). In this *vita*, which is written rather late in comparison to other *vitae* of saints which typically date to the 12th century, the encounter of Gwyn ap Nudd and St Collen is described.

St Collen was Abbot of Glastonbury, but after some time he retreated into the wilderness, a typical resort for a saint, and tried to lead a contemplative life. This was disturbed by people who spoke about Gwyn in front of his door, crediting Gwyn with the title of a king of Annwn. But Collen reproached the people for talking about Gwyn, as he considered Gwyn to be no better than the devil. To make a long story short, Collen was finally summoned by Gwyn to appear on the summit of a hill at high noon. There he found a wonderful castle and Gwyn sitting on a golden chair, the knights and servants of the king all handsome and the king's men dressed in red and blue.

Collen, however, refused to eat, for he claimed the food was but the leaves of the trees. Moreover, he claimed that the red and blue of the king's men's clothes signified burning and coldness. Thereupon Collen started to spray holy water he had brought with him in a flask, and immediately found himself alone on the mountain top.

Though the tale shows Gwyn ap Nudd as a splendid king of Annwn, it is full of religious metaphors and is designed as a story of exorcism, considering Gwyn equal to a devil or a demon-king. The world of Gwyn is an illusionary one. In this the classical Welsh fairy-tale motif (Sikes 1880) meets with the medieval doctrine that the devils create illusions to divert the pious monks (diNola 1993, 224). The hour Gwyn ap Nudd summons Collen is the hour in which the '*daemonum meridianum*', 'the demon of high noon', is active, a demonic character believed to specialise in seducing monks to forfeit their pious life, as Evagrius Ponticus writes (third century A.D.). The interpretation of the colours red and blue as hellfire and coldness is actually based on the association of hell with both freezing and burning. This is an ancient idea; the Venerable Bede interpreted the words of the scripture 'weeping and gnashing of teeth' (Luke 13, 28) as twofold pains of hell resulting from an excess of heat and coldness respectively (BED).

All this is quite in accordance with the earlier tale *Culwch ac Olwen*, whose redactor classed the inhabitants of Annwn as devils. Moreover, if we follow Elissa Henken's suggestion that the Welsh saint takes the place of the hero of society (Henken 1987; Henken 1991), we see that Gwyn is again representing the powers and forces outside the God-given order of society.

It is the author of *Buchedd Collen* who locates Gwyn's realm at Glastonbury, a fact which has great consequences for the neo-pagan traditions of our time.

Speculum Christiani

The *Speculum Christiani* text, dating back to the 14th century (Roberts 1980/1), is the bridge to folklore, for it describes how the people invoked Gwyn ap Nudd in cases when illness was inflicted by means of the 'Evil Eye'. The text fragment as edited by Brinley Roberts reads (Roberts 1980/1):

> *Quidam etiam stulti et stulte cum aliquis egrotauerit vadunt ad hostium tenentes igne et ferrum in manibus suis et clamant ad regem Eumenidium et reginam eius qui sunt maligni spiritus sic dicentes. Gwynn ap Nwdd qui es ultra in silvis pro amore concubine tue permitte nos venire domum. In hoc stultissime agunt petendo auxilium a malis spiritibus qui non habent nisi dampnacionem eternam contra clamat apostulus, Nolo vos socios esse demoniorum.*

> *Some stupid people also stupidly go to the door holding fire and iron in the hands when someone has inflicted illness, and call to the king of the Benevolent Ones and his queen, who are evil spirits, saying: 'Gwyn ap Nudd who are far in the forests for the love of your mate allow us to come home'. In this they are acting most stupidly that they ask help of the evil spirits which have nothing but eternal damnation [and] against whom the Apostle cries out 'We do not want to be the fellows of the demons'. [transl. A.R.]*

The author locates Gwyn's realm as '*ultra in silvis*', 'far in the forests'. Moreover, Gwyn can be moved by begging in the name of his love. Gwyn is addressed as '*Rex Eumenidum*', which is an *interpretatio Graeca* (Greek interpretation) of the nature of his subjects implying that they are avenging spirits who must be addressed with an appeasing name. 'Eumenides' is a classical Greek term which means literally the 'Benevolent Ones' or 'Gracious Ones' and was used to address the Erinyes, the avenging goddesses. The author of the *Speculum Christiani* text had most certainly a classical education and thus he seems to have translated the Welsh folk belief into a classical Greek term, for he seems to have looked for a term to translate '*plant Annwn*' into Greek or Latin.

This passage reinforces all information we have from the other sources: Gwyn is dwelling in the wilderness beyond the cultivated fields. In this context it is certainly worthwhile considering that J. Gwenogvryn Evans pointed out in the preface to his edition of the *Black Book of Carmarthen* (1922) that there existed an idea of locating *Annwn*, Gwyn's kingdom, in the forests of the North. Gwyn ap Nudd is filled by a deep reverence for his queen/mistress. His subjects are potentially dangerous and of great vindictiveness – a trait which is persistent for the Welsh Fair Folk and attested even after the name of their king vanished from folklore (Gruffudd 1958).

The *Speculum Christiani* text was written for the instruction of clerics. Actually it is the only source relating a folk custom – dimly outlined – involving Gwyn ap Nudd. This text and the references to Gwyn in poetry show that Gwyn must have played a role in Welsh folklore and oral tradition, and he must have been more widely known, for it would make no sense to use him as a reference point either in instructions for the clerics or in poetry if he was not widely known. However, Gwyn has totally vanished from folklore since then. The collectors of fairy folktales do not report any (new) fairy stories involving Gwyn (Rhys 1901; Sikes 1880; Thomas 1908; Evans-Wentz 1911; Owen 1887; Evans 1944). There are no tales or evidence in the sound archives of St Fagans, National History Museum of Wales, regarding Gwyn either (PC).

The images used in *Buchedd Collen* probably hold the key for understanding Gwyn's disappearance. With the meaning of 'Annwn' changing from 'Otherworld' to 'Hell', he might have been absorbed into the traditional figures and names used for the Christian devil. The way in which fairies are depicted in *Buchedd Collen* is of great similarity to their description in *Gweledigaethau y Bardd Cwsg* (*The Visions of the Sleeping Bard*, 1703) by Ellis Wynne (Wynne 1998). The fairies of Ellis Wynne perform their activities on a 'twmpath' (hillock; mound) ('tumpath chwarae' precisely, which denotes a village green or playing field (GPC)). The castle of Gwyn was also located on a 'tumpath', a hillock, according to *Buchedd Collen*, which uses this special expression and also reports about the red and blue garments of Gwyn's subjects. But in Wynne's text they are called subjects to Belial, who is described as *Tywysog Annwn* (Prince of Annwn), and Lucifer is given the same title, whereas Gwyn was known as *Brenin Annwn* – King of Annwn. These titles are close enough in meaning to suggest that Gwyn's name was dropped in favour of the conventional Christian names for the Devil.

The time of Romanticism (19th and early 20th centuries)

We do not find any new sources related to Gwyn until the time of the Classical Revival in the 18th century. At that time the medieval bardic traditions had completely ended, but the idea of bringing classical learning into Welsh literature was continued from the time of the Renaissance. Leaving behind the Renaissance interest for discovering only objective truths, antiquarians, Iolo Morganwg among them, tried to recreate the Welsh past in a new romantic image (Johnston 1999). In the time of the Classical Revival, Iolo Morganwg styled him in a Triad into one of 'the blessed astronomers' of the Isle of Britain (MYV).

> *Tri Gwyn Seronyddion ynys Pridain:*
> *Idris Gawr, a Gwydion mab Don, a Gwyn ap Nudd;*
> *A chan faint eu gwybodau am y ser a'u hanianau a'i hansoddau y darogenynt*
> *a chwennychid ei wybod hyd yn nydd brawd.*

Three blessed astronomers of the Isle of Britian:
Idris the giant, and Gwydion mab Don, and Gwyn ap Nudd,
And so great was their knowledge about the stars and their nature and
their qualities that they prophesied that which one desired to know
until the day of doom.

While we can speculate as to the origin of this idea, it is important to remember that Iolo is known to have invented a great amount of material which he then presented as 'traditional'. Thus, this idea may be based on the existence of a Neolithic earthwork and the remains of a Bronze Age stone circle on Ynys Môn (Anglesey) called 'Bryn Gwyn' in the proximity of a stone called 'astronomer stone' (Nicholson 1840). These remains from the past are discussed in Henry Rowlands' *Mona Antiqua Restorata* (Rowlands 1766). Ynys Môn was known to have been a stronghold of the druids in pre-Roman times (Tacitus, *Annales* XIV, 30; TAA). Another element contributing to Iolo's ideas might be the tradition that the fairies are the souls of the druids, as related by W.Y. Evans-Wentz (1911) and Sikes (1880).

During the literary revival in the late 19th and early 20th centuries Elfed wrote his famous poem *Gwyn ap Nudd* (1895) which gave Gwyn back to literature (Elfed 1920; Williams 1978) and, even more, remembered all the old sources in Welsh language, as the poem expands on them. Elfed calls Gwyn ap Nudd 'Tywysog pob direidi', 'Prince of all mischief', evoking the vindictiveness and potential danger associated with the Fair Folk in folk beliefs (*cf.* also Gruffudd 1958, second paragraph). In this and in associating Gwyn with nature the poem is grounded in genuine Welsh tradition regarding Gwyn ap Nudd.

Another romantic poem, *The Fairie's Song* by John Jenkins, also mentions Gwyn ap Nudd, but in a rather patriotic role and presiding over feasting and dancing fairies in the moonlight (Jenkins 1873). Thus Gwyn ap Nudd is brought closer to the Victorian idea of miniature fairies.

A late product of this new romanticism is certainly a piano concerto by J. Holbrooke based on a text by T.E. Ellis (Lord Howard de Walden) named 'The Song of Gwyn ap Nudd'. The central theme is the yearly combat of Gwyn and Gwythyr for Creiddylad (ELL).

Sir John Rhys (1840-1915)

In the 19th century research in Celtic Studies strengthened, and Sir John Rhys, a Welsh scholar, became the first Professor of Celtic at Oxford University. This formidable pioneer in the field of collecting folklore and research in Celtic Studies would have a profound impact upon the image of Gwyn ap Nudd ('this repellent personage', as Rhys called him (Rhys, 1888, 560)) like no other.

It is consistent with Gwyn's disappearance from folklore that there are almost no references to Gwyn in Sir John Rhys's great work on Celtic folklore, *Celtic Folklore – Welsh and Manx* (1901).

But there are a great number in his *Studies in the Arthurian Legend* (1991) and in *Lectures on the Origin and Growth of Religion as illustrated by Celtic Heathendom* (1888).

In accordance with the fashion of the time, he believed it was possible to rediscover the deities of the pre-Christian time in disguise in the Arthurian tales. Moreover, his work was strongly guided by a comparative assessment of mythology in which the Roman and Greek mythology represented a sort of implicit standard.

Searching for a Celtic Hades and knowledge of Welsh folk beliefs, but certainly also the shift of meaning of Annwn from 'otherworld' to 'hell', and in a further interpretation to 'abyss, Hades', finally led Sir John Rhys to mistranslate and misread the earliest source, the poem from the *Black Book*. I could discuss a number of distortions of the original text in his translation, but I will focus here on those with the greatest impact. Rhys translates the words of Gwyn, who is coming from a battle and lamenting the warriors of the Old North with the words 'I am [alive], they [are] in the grave' (*Mi. wi wiw. vintev y bet*), as 'I am the escort of the grave' (Rhys 1891, 383). This and the fact that Gwyn is coming from a battle he has taken part in, telling about other battles he has been present at, is sufficient for Rhys to style Gwyn a psychopomp, a God of carnage, a Hades. The other distortions are the misreading of Gwyn's dog's name, 'Dormarch', as *Dormarth* and translating this as 'Death's Door' (Rhys 1891, 155-6) based on a spurious etymology – an idea already contested by J. Gwenogvryn Evans and Professor Foster (Evans 1922; Foster 1953). Rhys ignores the white horse of Gwyn and neglects the connotation of the term *gwyn* as 'blessed', reducing it to the colour 'white' (Rhys 1888, 84), and interprets this as the white of winter, death and mourning. However, in the saga poetry *gwyn* is often found as an epithet of the formidable hero, e.g. *Pwyll Wyn, Cai Wyn, Cynddylan Wyn*, also *Seiriol Wyn*, a saint's name, and even the expression Christ Wyn can be found.

As for the tale *Culwch ac Olwen*, Rhys focused much on the idea that Gwyn is riding the black sea-going horse Du y Moroedd on the boar hunt. The Welsh folk belief that the devil is able to manifest as a black horse (Rhys 1891, 70) is used by Rhys to corroborate Gwyn ap Nudd's image as a sinister character. He also believed he had discovered that Gwyn was the representative of the winter season, as he thought Gwyn's opponent Gwythyr to be a 'solar deity' in disguise (Rhys 1888, 561).

In Arthurian legend Rhys associated Gwyn largely with several characters all linked to the idea of the 'waste land' as realm of death and destruction (Rhys 1891, 120), but he also understood Gwyn to be an equivalent to Melwas, the king of the 'Summerland', based on the theme of the abduction of a lady, Queen Gwenhyfar, and that Melwas's stronghold was Glastonbury (Rhys 1891, 342).

He understood St Michael as a Christian replacement of Gwyn, due to his function as psychopomp (Rhys 1891, 341) and leader of a host – a fact which comes over as a certain contrast to the former, darkened image of Gwyn.

In his *Lectures on the Origin and Growth of Religion as illustrated by Celtic Heathendom*, he even equates him to Pluto, Cernunnos and Heimdallr, postulating for the first time a similarity to a horned deitiy (Rhys 1888, 84). These ideas were taken up by Charles Squire and have found and find quite a far distribution (Squire 2003, 254).

Robert Graves (1895-1985)

Robert Graves makes use of Celtic tradition in a way that is strongly biased by his pre-knowledge of Greek, Roman and Oriental mythology. Moreover, he seems to be influenced by the ideas of Frazer (Frazer 2003) about the dying God and by the ideas of the Cambridge Ritualists (Doty 2000, 337).

As a consequence, the yearly combat of Gwyn and Gwythyr for Creiddylad at the calends of May (*Calan Mai*) until the day of doom was the piece of information about Gwyn ap Nudd which would fit him into Graves' monomyth of the two heroes/gods competing for the threefold goddess in a seasonal combat (Graves 1975). He takes this core motive from *Culhwch ac Olwen* and, by focusing on this simple and widespread plot – namely two men fighting for a (divine) female, he successfully adapts Gwyn into his monomyth and opens the way for a rather wide syncretism by suggesting a few missing details.

He invents death and a burial rite for Gwyn as a dead hero (Graves 1975, 179), joins him in a Triad with characters of the Fourth Branch of the Mabinogi, Lleu and Dylan (Graves 1975, 321), and this finally makes Gwyn equal to the dying vegetation deities of ancient Greece and the ancient Near East, such as Dionysos, Osiris, Attis and Tammuz. He claims Gwyn to be equivalent to Osiris. Moreover, he is now fused into a 'white' threefold-god and is simultaneously linked to Gwythyr in an indissoluble dualism.

Gerald Gardner (1884–1964)

Gerald Gardner is one of the glamorous figures in the history of neo-paganism and played a crucial role in the development of Wicca (Hutton 1999). Gwyn ap Nudd is assigned a key role by Gardner, who sees in him the 'God of the Witches' as leader of the Spectral Hunt. Gardner states Gwyn ap Nudd to be 'one of the most famous of his [the god of the witches] names' (Gardner 2004, 145).

It is very obvious that Gardner is drawing strongly on the ideas of Sir John Rhys, but he takes things even further than Rhys and Graves. If Gwyn had been a god of death for Rhys, Gardner made him over into a 'God of Death and Resurrection' (Gardner 2004, 146), and if Gwyn was in Graves' monomyth subjected to death and resurrection, he is now the lord guiding the souls from and into life in our world. The god of the witches is also understood as a character holding a dualism of features, and Gardner assigns the aspect of the Dark God to Gwyn, and associates him clearly with the realm of death (Gardner 2004, 147). Indeed, the god of the witches in general rules over death, winter and autumn (Gardner 2008). His life-engendering aspect is acknowledged, but not equally stressed compared with his destructive side (Gardner 2004, 150), which is all in all a clear repetition of the ideas of Sir John Rhys.

Gwyn as an equivalent to Horus seems to be a new idea introduced by Gardner. Moreover, a central issue is the fact that Glastonbury should be Gwyn's abode according to *Buchedd Collen*. Gardner postulates Glastonbury to be the home of a (prehistoric) pre-Christian witch cult (Gardner 2004, 146).

Conclusions and consequences

From the given evidence we see that there is a set of medieval and early modern sources which, when investigated and explored, can be shown to have given rise to secondary sources. At the same time the authors of these secondary sources 'process' the given information considerably, thus changing features of Gwyn ap Nudd. This results in a change of both the characteristics attributed to him and a strong conceptual change.

The new attributes he is equipped with are most easily detected when skimming over the output of booklets and leaflets offered at places like Glastonbury, i.e. places which are strongly connected with Gwyn, or by skimming over the neo-pagan pages on the internet. We find attributes like 'Dark God', 'Guardian of the Doors between the Worlds', 'Winter King/God of Summer', 'Horned God', 'Welsh Angel of Death', etc. All those titles are certainly not supported by the early sources. The only attribute surviving almost undisturbed is that of the hunter.

Moreover, Gwyn is subjected to a significant conceptual change by Graves and Gardner. Graves assigns him the role of one of the protagonists in the seasonal ritual drama, a constructive element for an agrarian society. Gardner introduces him as 'God of the Witches', a character playing a key role in the religious rituals of Wicca, thus supporting the religious structure of a social group sharing this faith.

However, these are functions which cannot be reconciled with a character who is a member of the 'World of the Outlaw', representing the counter-concept to society. Such a character will be in conflict with the representatives of established religion (pagan or Christian) rather than supporting it (Nagy 1985, 83/4).

Even taking into account that Gwyn is assigned a destructive element in the tale *Culhwch ac Olwen*, he is by no means a Hades or a god mediating the transit of souls from and into the Otherworld as Gardner wants to see him, for this would make Gwyn a character who is upholding 'this world' as it is and in which death plays its part. In *Culhwch ac Olwen*, however, Gwyn is obviously a character who symbolises the end of all things, and certainly the ritual-accompanied circles of birth, life and death, and in this his title *Brenin Annwn*, King of the Non-

World, describes things rather accurately, as '*an-*' is a prefix which can negate so that a possible interpretation of the Welsh term Annwn is '*an+dwfn*' = 'Non-World' (GPC; Koch 2006).

We can see that this modern understanding of Gwyn is actually very far from the image the original Welsh sources suggested, which depicts Gwyn as a typical ruler of the 'Non-World', a figure ultimately in contrast to the well-ordered human sphere and strange to any ritual integral to the religion of society and the world of men.

The idea that the world of the Fair Folk is a contrast to the human world may have actually been deeply rooted in the original Welsh folklore, as illustrated by the *Itinerarium Cambriae* (*Journey through Wales*, 1191) by Giraldus Cambrensis (Gerald of Wales) (IC).

The presbyter Elidorus relates – according to Gerald of Wales – that the Fair Folk have no religious cult, but only have truth as their religion: they do not take oaths, they do not lie, they have no sun nor moon. Their world is a counter-concept to the world of men, who of course have a religion, take oaths, lie, violate the truth and live in the light of sun and moon.

Gwyn ap Nudd can be explained against this background in all his ambiguity. We are shown a peerless hero, a wise counsellor, an outstanding hunter-warrior with supernatural powers, a splendid king; an ardent lover on the one hand, on the other hand vindictive, dangerous, even cruel; he takes people and leads the fearsome Spectral Hunt, and in all those characteristics he exceeds the human measure of things, the measure of 'this world'.

With these lines which have led us back to the image of Gwyn from the early Welsh sources, I will close this concise analysis of the most important changes Gwyn has been subject to during the last 900 years, a process which is still going on, for Gwyn is again increasingly the subject of art and literature due to the strengthening of neo-pagan beliefs.

In general, monitoring this process might be a model study to help us understand better the processes to which fictional/mythological characters may be subjected. It might also encourage a critical assessment of the ways in which fictional characters are interpreted today and have been interpreted in the past.

· ·

Dr Angelika H. Rüdiger

Abbreviations

BC   Hafod MS 19, fol. 141 ff (written in 1536); Llanstephan MS 117, fol. 183, (1544-52), Lanst. MS 34, fol. 315 (copied by Roger Morys, towards the end of 16th cent.), Llanst. 18, fol. 25; Cardiff MS 36, fol 377, National Library of Wales, Aberythwyth

Hafod MS 19 published in *Lives of the British Saints* (Baring-Gould and Fisher), VI, 375. Y Greal (London, 1805-7), pp.337-41.

'*Rhyddiaith Gymraeg*', *Y Gyferol Gyntaf*, *Detholion o Lawsgrifau (1488-1609)*, Caerdydd, Gwasg Prifysgol Cymru, 1954, pp.36-41.

BED   Beda Venerabilis, *In Lucae Evangelium Expositio* lib. iv cap xxiii 55.

DAG   Dafydd ap Gwilym: http://www.dafyddapgwilym.net/ (28.02.2011)

ELL   'The Song of Gwyn ap Nudd', poem by T.E. Ellis for Pianoforte & Orchestra. Op. 52. Material added to the publishing of 'The song of Gwyn ap Nudd' by Hyperion. Records in the series 'The Romantic Piano concerto, Vol. 23'

GPC   Geiriadur Prifysgol Cymru http://www.wales.ac.uk/dictionary/ (09.08.2012)

IC   'Itinerarium Cambriae, seu laboriosae Balduini Cantuariensis archiepiscopi per William legationis accurate description auctore S. Giraldo Cambrense. Cum annotationibus D. Poweli. (vita Girali Cambrensis ex ejus scriptis, lelando et Baleo collecta.) [edited by Sir R. C. Hoare, Bart.]', British Library, Historical Print Editions

MWG   D.S. Evans, *A Grammar of Middle Welsh*, The School of Celtic Studies Dublin Institute For Advanced Studies 1989

MYV   Owen Jones, Edward Williams, and Williams Owen Pughe, 'Myvyrian Archaiology of Wales', Denbigh 1870, Thomas Gee

     http://archive.org/stream/myvyrianarchaiol00joneuoft#page/n5/mode/2up (25.03.2012)

PC   Personal communication from Dr R. Gwyndaff after a request at the Welsh National Museum for Folklore at St Fagan's

TAA   P. Cornelius Tacitus, *Annales*; source text: http://www.thelatinlibrary.com/tac.html (10.09.2012)

References

Bartrum, P.C., *A Welsh Classical Dictionary* (The National Library of Wales, 1993)

Bromwich, R. (ed.), *Trioedd Ynys Prydein* (Cardiff: University of Wales Press, 1961)

Bromwich, R. and Evans, D. (eds), *Culhwch ac Olwen* (Caedydd: Gwasg Prifysgol Cymru, 1997)

Chadwick, N., 'Imbas Forosnai' in *Scottish Gaelic Studies*, J. Macdonald (ed.), Vol. III, (Edinburgh: Humphrey Milford/ Oxford University Press, 1931), p.132.

Davies, S. (trans.), *The Mabinogion* (Oxford: Oxford University Press, 2007)

Denholm-Young, N., *Handwriting in England and Wales* (Cardiff, 1954), p.78 and note on pl. 16.

Doty, W.G., *Mythography. The Study of Myth and Rituals* (Tuscaloos: University of Alabama Press, 2000)

Elfed, *Caniadau Elfed* (Caerdydd: Cwnmi Cyhoeddiadol Addysgol, 1909)

Evans, H., *Y Tylwyth Teg* (Liverpool: Hugh Evans a'i feibion, cfn., Gwasg y Brython, 1944)

Evans, J.G. (ed.), *The White Book Mabinogion: Welsh Tales and Romances reproduced from the Peniarth Manuscripts* (Pwllheli, 1907)

Evans, J.G. (ed.), *Facsimile and Text of the Book of Aneirin* (Pwllheli 1908)

Evans, J.G. (ed.), Mühlhausen, L. (annotations), *The Black Book of Carmarthen*. Copy of Ludwig Mühlhausen. Typewritten with handwritten annotations. (MS collection University Library Tübingen, 1922)

Evans-Wentz, W.Y., *The Fairy-Faith in Celtic Countries* (1911; republished by Forgotten Books, 2007)

Frazer, J.G., *The Golden Bough. A study of magic and religion* (2003) http://www.gutenberg.org/ebooks/3623 (19.04.2012)

Foster, I.L., 'Gwynn ap Nudd', in G. Murphy, *Duanaire Finn*, Part III, Appendix G, (Dublin: Educational company of Ireland, 1953)

Gantz, J., *The Mabinogion* (London: Penguins Books, 1976), p.21.

Gardner, G., *The Meaning of Witchcraft* (Red Wheel/Weiser, York Beach, ME, 2004)

Gardner, G., *The Gardnerian Book of Shadows* (republished by Forgotten Books, 2008)

Graves, R., *The White Goddess* (New York, Farrar, Strauss & Giroux, renewed edition 1975)

Gruffydd, W.J., *Folklore and Myth in the Mabinogion. A lecture delivered at the National Museum of Wales on 27 October 1950* (Cardiff: University of Wales press, 1958)

Henken, E.R., *Traditions of the Welsh Saints* (Cambridge: D.S. Brewer, 1987)

Henken, E.R., *The Welsh Saints – A Study in Patterned Lives* (Cambridge: D.S. Brewer, 1991)

Higley, S., *Preiddeu Annwn – The Spoils of Annwn. Text and translation.* http://www.lib.rochester.edu/camelot/preideu.html (2012)

Hughes, H.D. *Hynafiaethau Llandegai a Llanllechid* (Cyfoeddiadau Mei, 1979)

Hutton, R., *The Triumph of the Moon. A History of Modern Pagan Witchcraft* (Oxford: Oxford University press, 1999)

Huws, D., *Medieval Welsh Manuscripts* (University of Wales Press & National Library of Wales, 2000)

Jarman, A.O.H. and Jones, E.D., *Llyfr Du Caerfyrddin* (Caerdydd: Gwasg Prifysgol Cymru, 1982)

Jarman, A.O.H., 'LLyfr Du Caerfyrddin, The Black Book of Carmarthen', Sir John Rhys Memorial Lecture, in *Proceedings of the British Academy* (1985), vol. LXXI, pp.333-56.

Jarman, A.O.H., 'The heroic ideal in early Welsh poetry' in Meid, W. (ed.), *Beiträge zur Indogermanistik und Keltologie* (Innsbruck, 1967), pp.193-211.

Jenkins, J., *The poetry of Wales* (Llandidloes: John Pryse, 1873) (ebook #18523, project Gutenberg, release date: 6 June 2006) http://infomotions.com/etexts/gutenberg/dirs/1/8/5/2/18523/18523.htm

Johnston, D., *The Literature of Wales* (Cardiff: University of Wales Press & Western Mail, 1999)

Jones, T.G., *Welsh Folklore and Folk-Custom* (second edn) (Cambridge: D.S. Brewer, 1979)

Koch , J., *Celtic culture. A historical encyclopedia*, Vol. 1 (Oxford UK, 2006)

Murphy, G., *Duanaire Finn*, Part III (Dublin: Educational Company of Ireland, 1953), pp.LXXVI-LXXVII

Nagy, J.F., *The wisdom of the Outlaw* (Berkley-Los Angeles-London: University of California Press, 1985)

Nagy, J.F., 'Fenian Heroes and their Rites of Passage', in Almqvist, B., Ó Catháin, S. and Ó Héalaí, P. *The Heroic Process* (Dublin: Glendale press, 1987), p.161.

Nicholson, E., 'Cambrian Traveller's Guide, in every direction' (London, third edn, 1840)

Di Nola, A., *Der Teufel* (München: Deutscher Taschenbuchverlag, 1993)

Owen, E., *Welsh Folk-Lore* (1887; PA: Norwood Editions/Norwood, 1973, reprinted by Kessinger Publishing)

Rees, A. and Rees, B., *Celtic Heritage* (New York: Thames and Hudson, 1961)

Rhys, J., *Lectures on the Origin and Growth of Religion as illustrated by Celtic Heathendom* (London: Williams and Norgate, 1888, reprinted by Kessinger Publishing, 2008)

Rhys, J., *Studies in Arthurian Legend* (Oxford: Claredon Press, 1891; reprinted by Kessinger Publishing 2008)

Rhys, J., *Celtic Folklore Welsh and Manx* (first published 1901; reprinted by Forgotten Books 2007)

Roberts, B.F., 'Rhai o Gerddi Ymddiddan Llyfr du Caerfyrddin' in Bromwich, R. and Jones, R.B., *Astudiaethau ar yr Hengerdd* (Caerdydd: Gwasg Prifysgol Cymru, 1978) pp.281, 311-18.

Roberts, B.F., 'Gwyn ap Nudd' in *Llên Cymru*, XIII (Ionor-gorffennaf, 1980-1), pp.283-9.

Rowland, J., *Early Welsh Saga Poetry* (Cambridge: D.S. Brewer, 1990)

Rowlands, H., 'Mona Antiqua Restaurata' (London: J. Knox, second edn, 1766); http://archive.org/details/monaantiquarest00lhuygoog

Sikes, W., *British Goblins* (first published 1880; reprinted by Forgotten Books 2007)

Skene, W.F. *The Four Ancient Books of Wales* (first edn 1868, Forgotten Books, republished 2007)

Squire, C., *Celtic Myth and Legend, Poetry and Romance* (Holicong PA, USA: Wildside Press, 2003)

Thomas, J., *The Welsh Fairy Book* (1908; reprint by Forgotten Books 2007)

Williams, I., *Canu Aneirin* (Caerdydd, Gwasg Prifysgol Cymru, 1970)

Williams, G., *An introduction to Welsh Literature* (University of Wales Press on behalf of the Welsh Arts Council, 1978)

Wynne, E., *Gweledigaethau y Bardd Cwsg* (Gwasg Gomer, Llandysul, 1998)

Websites

A short selection of internet pages in proof of Gwyn's image within neo-pagan beliefs:

www.mysteriousplanet.net/mysterious-west-of-e.php

www.gwynapnudd.com

www.glastonbury-pilgrim.co.uk/gwyn-ap-nudd.php [Winter King]

www.terrapsych.com/gods.html [god of hunt and fallen warriors]

www.oppapers.com/essays/Hades-And-Gwynn-Ap-Nudd/641995

www.celtnet.org.uk/gods_g/gwyn.html [Welsh angel of Death]

www.kathyjones.co.uk/glastonburygoddess.html [Gwyn riding at Midsummer time]

www.cyberwitch.com/Wychwood/PlantBran/tax.htm

http://tribes.tribe.net/gwynapnudd/thread/b7440456-735e-461e-9656-bb498bcb3fed [Gwyn god of summer]

Margaret Jones,
*The Quest for
Olwen*, p.49.

Friedrich Perlberg,
'Weihnachtsabend
in Nürnberg'.

Count Stoneheart and the first Christmas tree

Kate Forsyth

A retelling of a traditional German folktale by Kate Forsyth. This story was originally retold as 'The Christmas Fairy of Strasburg' by J. Stirling Coyne (1803-68).

A long time ago, in a small kingdom in Germany, there lived a young and handsome count, named Stoneheart by his people because he never fell in love, not once, no matter how pretty the girls brought to his notice.

One snowy Christmas Eve, Count Stoneheart and his court rode out to hunt in the great forest that surrounded his castle. They galloped deep into the forest, deeper than they had ever ridden before, till they were far from home. A white hart leaped through the forest, and Count Stoneheart whipped up his horse and raced after it, his courtiers streaming behind him. The hart ran so fast and so far that the hunt could not keep up; soon only Count Stoneheart was still in pursuit.

Then the hart leapt through a hedge of thorns and disappeared. Count Stoneheart found himself alone in the forest, with no idea of the way home. For as far as the eye could see, the trees stretched, black against the white. A raven called. Twilight fell.

In the clearing ahead was a pool of green water, somehow free of the ice that hung from every twig and thorn. Count Stoneheart dismounted and knelt by the pool to drink. To his surprise, the water was warm. He dipped both hands in, so he could wash his face, and felt a small, soft hand grasp his, slipping from his finger the ring he always wore.

Amazed, the Count sat back on his heels, staring into the pool. He saw a quick glimpse of the most enchantingly beautiful face he had ever seen, surrounded by swirling tendrils of black hair. The woman in the pool smiled at him, then turned and dived, with a flash of small bare feet.

In the distance, Count Stoneheart heard the call of the hunting horns and the baying of the hounds. He sat still, however, staring into the pool, calling to the woman to return.

It was not long before his courtiers found him, sitting in the twilight by a pool that steamed gently in the freezing air. Together they rode back to the castle, all filled with amazement at his story of the mysterious woman in the pool who had taken his ring.

'You must have found the Fairy Well,' said the oldest and wisest of his councillors. 'It has been a long time since I have heard of it.'

'You must be careful,' said his old nursemaid. 'One shouldn't meddle with the Fair Folk. Nothing good will come of it.'

'We shall ride to the well in the morning and drain it dry,' cried the castle constable. 'How dare those fairies steal your ring!'

'I didn't mind,' the Count said, feeling again that soft hand in his.

When Count Stoneheart retired to bed that night, he could not sleep. He lay twisting and turning till midnight, when suddenly he heard the sound of the most beautiful music. He leapt up from his bed and, drawing his velvet cloak about him, ran down the stairs. A great hammering on the front doors resounded through the castle.

Count Stoneheart flung open the doors and saw before him a crowd of the strangest and most beautiful creatures he had ever seen. Some were tall and dressed in leaves, with flowers twined in their hair. Others were short and hairy, with squashed noses and eyes like slits. Some fluttered about in the air like huge butterflies, while others slithered in, their scaly bodies undulating like snakes. Leaping musicians played pipes and drums, and Count Stoneheart found himself standing in the midst of a wild and joyous dance, as his unexpected visitors twirled and whirled in through the door.

The fairy folk carried in a tall fir tree and set it in the centre of the hall, and then, holding hands, they danced about it. The tree was hung with glittering icicles and frost flowers that shone like stars in the candlelight. Count Stoneheart stood speechless, gazing at all this beauty and wonder.

Then the most beautiful woman Count Stoneheart had ever seen danced towards him, laughing. Dressed in a flowing mantle of green, she wore a crown of holly berries on her flowing, raven-black hair. 'I am Elfrieda, the Queen of the Fairies,' she said. 'I have come to return your midwinter visit, and to give back to you what was lost in the Fairy Well.'

She held out her hand and there in her palm was the lost ring. Count Stoneheart took back his ring and bent his head to kiss her soft palm, and she smiled and drew him into the dance.

All night the Count and the fairy queen danced about that mysterious glittering tree, the haunting music keeping all weariness from him. At last, at dawn, the singing and dancing stopped, and the fairy folk turned to flee. But Count Stoneheart seized Elfrieda's hand and would not let her go.

'Please stay with me,' he begged. 'I have fallen in love with you. Stay and be my bride.'

'I will stay with you,' Queen Elfrieda replied, holding both his hands in her own. 'For I too have fallen in love with you. However, you must make me a faithful promise. You must never say the word "death" in my presence. Can you swear that for me?'

'Of course,' the count replied, filled with joy.

They were married the very next day.

A year passed happily, and the Queen gave birth to a beautiful baby boy. Winter once again mantled the land with snow, and Count Stoneheart decided to go hunting in the forest on Christmas Eve, as he had done the previous year.

The horses were saddled and bridled and brought to the gate, but his wife was not ready.

Count Stoneheart waited impatiently, the horses stamping their hooves and blowing white steam through their nostrils. Still the Queen was not ready. The dogs shivered and whined, and the huntsmen rubbed their hands together and blew into them. Still the Queen was not ready.

At last, as the last of the daylight slipped away, the Queen came down, looking very beautiful in her green velvet riding dress and feathered hat.

Count Stoneheart cried, 'As slow as you are, you'd be a good messenger to send for Death!'

As soon as his wife heard the forbidden word on his lips, she gave a wild cry. A whirlwind caught her up and bore her away. Desperately she caught at the stone archway above the castle gate, trying to stay, but the wind was too strong. She disappeared into the dusk, only the sound of her scream lingering in the air.

Although Count Stoneheart searched all through the forest and all through the land, he never saw her again. All that was left of her was the imprint of her small hand in the stone archway.

Every Christmas Eve till he died, Count Stoneheart set up a fir tree in his great hall, and decorated it with sparkling jewels and lighted candles, to try and recapture the magic of the fairy tree. He would sit beside it with his son and tell him the story of how he had first met his mother, and how he had lost her through his pride and impatience. When his son grew up, he too celebrated Christmas with a fir tree from the forest, and the practice slowly spread throughout the land, till every house had its tree hung with shimmering lights each Christmas Eve.

Count Stoneheart's castle lies in ruins now, though the archway still stands, with the shape of a small, desperate hand still imprinted upon it.

. . . .

Kate Forsyth

My favourite story when I was young

Martine Hennard Dutheil de la Rochère

Being a sickly child, I read a lot in bed – as if for life, like David Copperfield. Aside from an enormous cookbook with colour illustrations of extraordinarily elaborate dishes and rococo pastries, my favourite book was an old, battered edition of Andersen's *La Reine des Neiges* (*The Snow Queen*) which probably belonged to my mother (it was published in 1945, when she was a little girl). For hours, I mused over the faded pastel illustrations, depicting a soft, magical world of snow flakes and blue ice, with a melancholic Queen who looked like a spectral version of Botticelli's Venus, and dreamy children in hazy landscapes that merged into the sky. What fascinated (and horrified) me was the tiny shard of glass that falls into Kay's eye, and penetrates into his heart, turning it into a cold, unfeeling, dead thing ('Il ne ressentait plus aucun mal, mais le verre était là'). It meant that the childlike pleasure of offering one's face to the sky to be kissed by falling snow held unsuspected dangers. Oddly, I also related it to my experience of the sickening smell of ether, its cold sensation on the skin, the white sheets and cotton swabs, the glass syringe in its shiny metal bowl, the woolly doze, numb pain, hollowness, absence. Kay's death-in-life state was such an intimate projection of my own reality. Of course, there were other images too: the children's special place, high up above the street where the balconies are linked by a bower of flowers; the painted roses in the old woman's hat that remind Gerda of her mission to rescue her friend; the robber's daughter who caresses the deer's neck with her sharp knife and yet helps Gerda in her quest; the message that the Finn woman writes to the Sami woman on a piece of dried cod …

But Kay was the character that intrigued me the most. After all, he survives (or does he?) but is transformed, perhaps forever, unless Gerda's tears really bring about some reverse transformation at the end. Though the narrator unfavourably contrasts Kay's uneasy humour and unsentimental nature (against Andersen's own sentimentalism) with Gerda's unfailing love, courage and determination, Kay also gains something in his strange travels and brush with death. After all, he is given a unique opportunity to stay for a while in the Queen's ice palace. He also admires the beauty of the frosted flowers on the window-pane, marvels at the elaborate symmetry of star-like snowflakes, and later enjoys the lone pleasure of composing geometrical figures in vast rooms lit by the aurora borealis. If he manages to write the word 'eternity', says the Queen, he will be his own master and get a new pair of skating shoes. Somehow, I sensed a personal message in this marvellous, empty and silent palace which also chills the heart, and in the never-ending jigsaw puzzle (also a familiar activity for a homebound child) wondered:

Edmund Dulac's 'Snow Queen', in Hans Christian Andersen's *The Snow Queen and Other Stories* (London: Hodder & Stoughton, 1911).

what if Kay had remained in the ice palace forever? Would he have solved the mysterious charade? There is a strange appeal at the heart of Andersen's fairy tales, and something sick and sinister too, otherworldly and strangely close to the bone. Perhaps because the author knew that fairy tales are stories to think with. Feel with. And to die for, even.

. . . .

Martine Hennard Dutheil de la Rochère

Mel Grant,
'*Hearne*'.

Herne

Steve O'Brien

In high autumn toadstools constellate the woods, red and white, yellow and brown. The leaves lie among them like gloves of the dead.

There is a forest, or the remnant of one, that has been overlaid by county borders – Surrey, Hampshire and Buckinghamshire; but the forest does not know these invisible names – lines decreed by men. There is an oak amongst all the others, swag-girthed, limbs crazily angled, as if it has gone senile and is sprouting against all normal decorum. It is massive and lurches, in mid stagger, all alone in a clearing. The other trees stand in a circle, as at a respectful distance.

Here and there pieces of bark have fallen away revealing the white sapwood. One bare patch is so large that it resembles a doorway. Ivory bracket fungus juts like steps up the trunk and one massive beam casts out across the space, making a reaching shadow, even in the crisp noon. Almost a yard along this beam is a worn ring. It looks almost polished, as if a rope was once fastened there and a heavy load swung out across the gap.

This is Herne's Oak. Do not ask me where it stands. I will not tell you. Trees of the same name were planted by Queen Victoria and her playboy son Edward. These were mere fancies; a royal attachment to half-forgotten lore. There have been many famous and illustrious men who have looked for this tree; yet, among them all, it was only Will Shakespeare who found it lurking in its musky glade. It was an old oak, even in his time – older, perhaps, than he knew.

The reason that royalty have held the image of this tree so highly in their imaginations is that it is reputed to hold a doom for them. If it falls they and their house will also fall. And because they have never found the true oak, they plant saplings that grow into false totems in and around Windsor Park. Meanwhile, with splendid contempt the true Oak thrives, in a slow sap-ticking time all of its own, away in a neglected stand of the forest that once covered all England. There have been no axes here. These trees have never flinched at the sound of a saw. All the paths seem to veer away from this relic heartwood.

Let us suppose that, by chance, you do hack your way off the guide book trail, through the bracken and brambles, and get close enough to ponder the corrugated bark, the clawed branches and the ring-burned beam. Keep an eye on the November light as it needles through the woods. Turn away between two and three, before darkness begins to fall. Find the path and do not look back. I know you will. The forest teems with clicks and snaps – the flick of a squirrel, a thrush in a thicket. The evening comes quickly, like a velvet sheet drawn over the bosk. A pheasant jirrs away from you. Its throttled cry tears the dusk. Of course you start. Of course you look behind. It suddenly seems a long way back to the pub car park, the stile and the laminated trail sign.

The sentinel trees stutter the dying light. Stop quite still. Back there in the glade something glints silver, as if a coin has been tossed in the gloaming. And what is that 'notch-notch' sound? A wind comes in the direction of the setting sun. It tries the collar and seams of your jacket. Turn from the wind and face the clearing. You can hear better with your mouth open. No cars hum in the distance, but there now is a heavy thump as a horse places its hoof. Then the unmistakable slink and chomp as it plays with the bit.

So here you are, standing open-mouthed, and there is a horse back there. It is a black and massive beast. You can see its haunches fractured by the trees. It is pacing the clearing, pawing the ground, snorting. You sense, rather than see it bucking its neck. You hear the trappings of its bridle. You want to cry out, to ask if there is someone there. But for some reason you do not speak. Instead you turn and strive for the path. The cold branches claw on either side. As your eyes begin to grope fear seems to hiss at you from every cleft and thorn.

'Notch-notch.' You suddenly place the sound. Antlers being sharpened, tested against a tree. It is, after all, autumn – the belling time. The horse continues to pace back there. Horse and stag? You fix on the fading eye of the red sun and aim for the car park half a mile away. Best not to run. You might snag your feet. Suddenly, there comes a yelp and whine of hounds crying in delicious anticipation. They are straining these dogs, their paws aching for the chase. The chase!

You run. Your legs are spurred by an urge so ancient it is deeper than fright. It is nameless and thoughtless. Your body reacts without permission or regard. You are running a narrow track. Twigs pull at your jacket, your hands, your face, but the scratches are painless. Only at the most tremendous crashing do you stop again and turn to look back.

A sight of deepest nightmare breaks from the stand of trees circling the clearing. Such a leaping picture is found only in the dim recesses of caves, where our ancestors splashed their fears across limestone in the colours of blood and charcoal. A stallion, sleek as liquid tar, rears through the saplings, sending beech leaves upwards in a vortex. A rider, booted, bearded, huge, spurs the beast. His sword takes the red of the sun. The stark antlers of a king stag thrust from his head. At his side three dogs, the colour of washed coal, bay the rising moon. Their fangs are white. Their eyes are crimson slits.

You take all this in the second before you turn and hare down the path, running as you have never run before. You are oblivious to the breath itching like rust in your lungs. You are blind to the snares and snatches of cruel wood. In your eyes there is only the lowest bleb of sunset, in your ears only the pounding of massive hooves and the hounds singing for your flesh.

. . . .

Say his name: 'Herne'. It comes like a threat of frost across the tongue. Or a wind that sharps when the rooks pause calling and there should be a silence in the trees. Herne. Scholars have attempted to trace his story back, but the strands of his tale are like a run of weedy ground elder leading ever deeper into the forest. In his play, *The Merry Wives of Windsor,* Shakespeare gives us a few muscular lines concerning the rider in the woods:

> There is an old tale goes, that Herne the hunter,
> Sometime a keeper here in Windsor forest,
> Doth all the winter time at still midnight,
> Walk around about an oak, with great ragg'd horns;
> And there he blasts the tree, and takes the cattle;
> And makes milch-kine yield blood, and shakes a chain
> In a most hideous and dreadful manner.

It is worth remembering that Will was once fined for poaching deer when he was a youth in Warwickshire. He knew the woods, knew the tawny heart of autumn. Windsor people would have told him the old tale:

> Why, yet there want not many, that do fear
> In deep of night to walk by this Herne's oak.

In the inns they would have told him that many years before, back in King Richard's time, there was a loyal keeper who accompanied his liege on deep forays to hunt boar and stag. One day they tracked spoor to a glade and there they came upon a white hart, ice-kissed and proud in the spring noon. The king drew his bow and shot, but the arrow went wide and caught the stag in the hind quarter. Blood fell on the snowdrops. The hart thrashed and roared. It lowered its tines and charged at the king, who stood transfixed and aghast. A shadow fell across his breast. It was his keeper, who had stepped in front to take the blow. Horn stabbed the keeper's doublet, sheared into his ribs. Again, blood spattered the snowdrops. But he had drawn his dagger and the blade flashed at the stag's white throat. This, they say, was Herne, who lay mortally injured under the hart, and had saved the life of Richard, his king.

They brought him back on the same cart on which the stag was thrown. Some say that a wizard appeared that night and ordered the hart's antlers to be fetched to Herne's bedside. The wizard tied the horns to Herne's head and said that although desperately ill he would heal. Sure enough, within a week he was strong again. The king, ever mindful of his reputation, promoted this Herne to head keeper. He returned to his work now dressed in a fine new hunting livery of deepest green, the envy of all the other keepers. But all was not well. Herne found that all his keen skills of tracking, his knowledge of wind and instinct for the direction of the herds had disappeared. At night he lay in his bed thrashing, as if in a fever. His dreams were all of chase and arrows and blood.

The other keepers, those jealous of his new livery and position, whispered to Richard; within weeks he fell from favour. The king dismissed Herne and banished him from the forest and parkland. Yet still Herne lingered there, particularly after dark, when the deer trod in slow state through the trees, under the white face of the moon. And so it happened that one night the band of keepers found Herne standing alone in the very glade where he had saved the king's life. They seized him, tied his wrists and slipped a noose over his head. They threw the rope over the beam of a sturdy oak at the centre of the glade and they hanged him. Laughing, they watched him kick and then they left his slumped body pendulous under the stars.

The next morning a young swineherd ran to the keepers and told them he had seen a man riding fast through the woods with antlers on his head and a pack of dogs at his heels. They went to the clearing and found an empty noose swinging in the wind.

At the fireside in the taverns the locals would have told Will Shakespeare how Herne's fierce ghost roamed wide across the counties of Hampshire, Surrey and Berkshire, seeking his revenge on all who stand in his way. A particular curse of his is reserved for the descendents of Richard, the monarchs who have fenced and tamed the woods.

The bones of this tale may have been good enough for Will to hang with the sturdy flesh of his poetry, but the story of a horned rider from the depths of the wood seems to have more to it than the revenge of a hanged keeper. Antlers and a fiery steed? A hoary tree and pitch-dark hounds? Like the sneaking tendrils of ground elder that twine along unseen tracks, some people believe that Herne can be followed back much further than King Richard's time, to ancient and unsettling origins.

· · · · · · · · · · · · · · · · · · · ·

'Herne'; say the name again. It is like a sudden gust of snow on naked skin, or the trembling minute between two clouts of thunder. There are those linguists who have skills to untangle old languages. They see the name Herne as a worn smooth version of 'Herian', which in turn is derived from the old Norse 'Einherja'. And here the chill begins to prickle at your neck. For 'Einherjar' means 'Leader of the slain' and is one of the guises of Odin the furious, Odin the smiter, Odin the fell god of the wilderness and mountains.

Odin, Wotan, Woden; all across the north of Europe, from the oak to the beech, from the ash to the pine, they used to worship him. When the English came to Britain their gods went before them into the forests and moors. Chief among them was their one-eyed, implacable Woden.

He is restless and vital, known for his trickery and cunning disguises. He has many faces, many forms, including this cold title: 'Hangatyr' – 'God of the Hanged'. Accordingly, there is a verse in the old poem, 'Havamal', that tells of a weird and gruesome consummation:

I know that I hung on a windy tree
nine long nights ...
... myself to myself,
on that tree of which no man knows ...

On the sacred oak Woden sacrificed himself to himself. Pinioned there, he fretted against his own divinity. He was pierced by his own spear. As he hung against the bark, the branches wrapped around his legs and arms. Ivy crawled over his skin and thorns stabbed his flesh. Lost in his agony he looked inwards down the hidden paths of his mind. Then on the ninth night he came down from the tree with knowledge. In the wilderness of his torment he had gained the secrets of the runes. For it was Woden, so our ancestors believed, this *God of the Hanged*, who brought writing to mankind.

. . . .

Hunters give clear whistles and shrill cries. They favour brass horns of high clarion. You can shout in a forest and the sound will blunt against the trees. How much more so with whispers? In November the leaves purse on the wind and one man conferring to another will find his tale taken and twisted. Stories pass down through centuries and sussurate against the years. The stories change. A Teutonic hanged god transmutes to a tale of a king, a white hart and a wronged keeper. Yet the sap of the truth can be tapped, and Herne, the 'Leader of the Slain', canters towards us in one more dread aspect.

. . . .

You are still running. The forest hunches in the smoky new darkness. The roots and branches still hiss at your limbs. The growing weakness in your chest must be denied if you are to gain the car park. Behind you the undergrowth thrashes and the hounds leap every fallen trunk in slavering joy. The horse plunges and the horned rider bends low with his mailed hand open, ready to snatch. He is literally at your heels.

You break onto the tarmac. Your Peugeot sleeps over by the wall of the pub. There are no lights on; no smoke from the chimney. The pub is closed. It is over. You trip, falling first on one knee, and then you feel the gravel bite your cheek. It is over. A hunted fox will run and run, but sooner or later it will fall, and then, ribs heaving, tongue lolling, it will turn and await the pack.

. . . .

From the carved homesteads of the Schwarzwald to shepherd huts in the Tatras Mountains, from rain-soaked cottages in the Cumbrian Fells to Basque villages under the crags of the Pyrenees there are tales of a relentless huntsman and his pack of hounds. In Germanic and

Nordic lands they are known as the Wild Hunt. A horned rider gallops the midnight sky, through bogs and vaulted glens. His prey is any traveller foolish enough to let darkness overtake his steps. More explicitly it is the wicked and those with guilty secrets who have the most to fear.

Everywhere the stories tell that the huntsman rides sinners down in lonely places. He grabs them by the scruff of the neck and carries them up into the shivering heights. The victim dangling at the pommel of the saddle might look behind and see the dogs coursing at their master's side. How they yelp and gnash in ecstasy. Behind them he might see other riders – gaunt figures with parchment skin and dreadful eyes. Moonlight picks out their horned helmets and tarnished breastplates. The dead ride in Herne's train. He is, after all, *'Einherjar'* – the Leader of the Slain. The victim is bound for hell.

. . . .

The stallion rears over you and when its hoof comes down sparks flash on the frosty gravel. You are on your back cringing. Your jacket is torn. The rider leans towards you across his creaking saddle. His horse snorts and shudders. He holds the dogs back with a sweep of one gauntlet. They snap and growl in disappointment. His black beard is woven with ivy. His antlers are fluttering velvet rags. His eyes hold nothing. They are empty. He speaks but no words are audible. His speech comes in an icy furl. He shouts noiselessly and sudden rime crackles on your scratched cheek. Then comes a moment more awful than all the preceding ones. He fixes you with his oblivion stare and sharp silence creeps over you. You cannot think. Terror floods your ears, your mouth. Say whatever prayers you can remember.

He straightens and looks about himself, looks up to the new stars. He points with his red sword and suddenly kicks his spurs. The horse rears again, but this time it does not descend. Instead it lifts. Impossibly the horse gallops upwards, bearing the huntsman over the tiled roof of the pub. The hounds follow, chasing on the air above your head. Their eager baying fades on the wind. Herne does not want you. You have been lucky.

. . . .

Steve O'Brien

Glasshopper by Isabel Ashdown, winner of the *Mail on Sunday* Novel Award.

University of Chichester

MA Creative Writing

Our MA in Creative Writing is designed to give students a structure within which they can develop both their writing and critical skills, experimenting with a range of possibilities available to the contemporary writer.

This is an exciting, imaginative course. Our students publish and win prizes. All written assignments, apart from the related commentaries on the process of producing the work, are creative.

Course content
The MA comprises four taught modules and a manuscript:
- The Writing Studio
- Metaphor and the Imagination
- Sources and Transformations
- Launching the Manuscript
- The Manuscript (a creative dissertation of 20,000 words)

Find out more
For more information visit **www.chi.ac.uk**, or contact Stephanie Norgate, Email: **s.norgate@chi.ac.uk**

Recent student successes
- Jac Cattaneo won the 2010 Royal Academy of Arts Short Story Competition with her story, 'Lessons in Tightrope Walking'
- Honoria Beirne's short story 'Shake Me, Shake Me' was short-listed for the Bridport Prize in 2010 and is now published in the prestigious Bridport Anthology
- Katherine Orr was the only student in the UK to win AHRC funding for her creative writing PhD, a collection of short fiction entitled *This Inland Sea*
- Isabel Ashdown's debut novel, *Glasshopper*, won the *Mail on Sunday* Novel Award
- Melanie Whipman won third prize in the New Writer Short Story Competition 2010 for her story 'Falafel'
- Gabrielle Kimm's novel, *The Courtesan's Lover*, is listed in the Top 100 paperbacks and was shortlisted for the Impress Prize for Fiction

Snap, Crackle and Pop in British Rice Krispies advertising.

Fig. 1 Heaps of Fun.
Fig. 2 'Someone's coming!'
Fig. 3 'Each one is made from a single grain of rice, and contains Vitamin D, which helps build bones!'

Fig. 3

Fig. 1

Fig. 2

Whatever happened to the pixies? The shrinking role of Snap, Crackle and Pop in British Rice Krispies advertising

Louise Jolly

Snap, Crackle and Pop have been bringing fairy themes into advertising since the 1930s, when they were first created in the US as a trio of pixie mascots for the breakfast cereal Rice Krispies. Their names onomatopoeically capture the sound the cereal makes when milk is poured on it, and have been translated into a whole range of equivalents for different cultures, such as Cric, Crac and Croc in France, Pif, Paf and Puf in Denmark and Knisper, Knasper and Knusper in Germany.

The historic role of the trio in Rice Krispies advertising shows just how culturally pervasive fairy-tale themes are. Cropping up in all kinds of contexts – marketing and advertising as much as literature, film and art – these themes show a continuing mutability and endurance that befits their origins in folk and oral tradition.

But despite their capacity for survival, they also encounter cultural moods which can be more or less supportive of their flourishing. For instance, in British advertising today, various pressures have shrunk the space available for Snap, Crackle and Pop to bring fantasy to the breakfast table. The story I want to tell here is about how an advertising ethos steeped in fantasy and magic met a cultural return to ideas of parental authority, realism and familial cohesion – with the role of the pixies being diminished as a result.

Of course, British culture in the wider sense remains enthralled by fantasy productions of every kind; this essay is by no means trying to construct a grand narrative of fantasy decline. The example of Snap, Crackle and Pop nevertheless highlights an interesting shift of mood in a very specific pocket of cultural expression, worth registering for the cultural dynamics it reveals.

Until recently, the trio played a big part in Rice Krispies advertising. In true pixie style, they enriched breakfast time with merry pranks and anarchic behaviour. In its advertisements, the cereal brand gave them full rein to express their pixie personalities, allowing them to pour explosive powder into cereal bowls, skid around the table on banana skins, and unleash all manner of havoc.

In more recent advertising, that's changed. The pixies have been sidelined in favour of realistic scenes of parents and children enjoying the famous sound of the cereal together. This shift in emphasis might sound simply like a new creative direction from the brand's advertising agency, but there's a more far-reaching cultural change going on here, revealing changing attitudes towards the family, parental authority and the relationship between fantasy and advertising. When these advertisements are set in the context of ethical changes in marketing discourse, Snap, Crackle and Pop become problematic – even, perhaps, a bit of an embarrassment. This isn't just about their own waning star either: there are wider implications here for the general status of fairy-tale and fantasy themes in marketing and advertising.

To begin, let's go back to the glory days of the trio. A close look at a couple of adverts from the 1990s shows what the pixies symbolised at this point – and how their antics affected family dynamics.

For instance, a 1999 advert shows the trio trying to throw Krispies through a moving target: a toast rack spun in the air by Crackle. Snap and Pop then skid across the table on a banana skin to illustrate the ad's theme, 'having heaps of fun' (Fig. 1). This quintessentially pixie-ish behaviour stems from age-old lore about the misbehaving spirits of the home – the tricksterish hobs and familiars who are both a help and a hindrance to the woman of the house.[1]

The difference here is that the woman of the house is nowhere to be seen, nor does any kind of parental figure appear to be on the premises. Instead, the pixies offer the child a 'home alone' fantasy, in which the normal rules of breakfast-time behaviour are suspended, and free play can reign.

The absence of the parental figure is crucial here, as it relates directly to the presence of the pixies. The pixies don't just allow the child to dream of freedom and anarchy – they're actually symbolically oppositional to the parent. Pixies and parents stand in an antagonistic relationship to each other: where pixies are, parents cannot be – and where parents are, pixies must surely disappear.

This mutually exclusive relationship emerges clearly in a 1996 advert focusing on the cereal's nutritional benefits. At first, it seems something completely different is happening in terms of the pixie-parent relationship. The pixies jump out of the box and begin to address 'Mum', saying they've come to put the record straight about the cereal's perceived lack of nutritional value. But the mother isn't there to listen; in fact, she's nowhere to be seen. And after the pixies deliver their little presentation on nutrition, they're startled by the sound of approaching footsteps (surely HER), which causes them to run off and jump back into their box (Fig. 2).

The same happens in a 1994 advert based on the story of the Sorcerer's Apprentice. A mother asks her son, Frankie, to tidy his room after breakfast – for which purpose he enlists the magical help of Snap, Crackle and Pop. The trio try to help out, but their irrepressible tendency to anarchy gets in the way – tidying just isn't in their nature (and again, we can see here the admixture of help and hindrance which Diane Purkiss describes as a feature of many household sprites). The important point here is that, as soon as the mother's voice is heard calling her son – "FranKEE!" – the pixies rush off into the cupboard to hide. Just the sound of her voice is enough to send them scurrying.

The implicit antagonism between mothers and pixies in these advertisements is charged with symbolic meaning. Even when we don't see the pixies avoiding the mother, we know the two parties are incompatible from the way they don't occupy the same frame (there may be exceptions – but this is definitely a strong pattern). The mother's presence may be off-stage or imminent but, however distant she is, the pixies flee as soon as she makes her presence felt.

This antagonism can be explored from a number of perspectives. Diane Purkiss, in *Troublesome Things*, provides a striking account of the fear with which mothers in the Middle Ages beheld supernatural beings – a fear with origins in changeling and abduction stories. There's a long tradition of the fairy (and pixies can be included under the fairy category here, as Purkiss does) being perceived by the mother as a 'threat to the nursery', Purkiss writes.[2] Babies and children were seen to be vulnerable to fairies: like fairies, the very young occupy the liminal symbolic space between life and death and so, like fairies, were felt to be somewhere outside the domain of the fully alive and the fully human.[3] This symbolic affinity meant fairies were always liable to snatch back their own.

If this is one of the ancient themes reverberating through Rice Krispies advertising, it follows that the pixies would need to run away from the mother. She mustn't know they are there, engaging in secret interaction with her children. For her to find out would almost certainly mean no more Rice Krispies in that particular household.

So the pixies represent a secret: a secret they share with the child, but that absolutely excludes the parents. With the 1996 advert on nutrition, things again seem to be different. The pixies seem to want to mediate between child and parent, defending a breakfast favourite to the mother on account of its healthy properties. But this step into new narrative territory is foiled when the pixies still run from the mother's approaching step at the end. There seems little doubt that their presence must be kept a secret from her.

Snap, Crackle and Pop therefore come to stand for a secret world carved out within the family home, a world all the more special to the child for the fact that parents don't know about it. The pixies offer something very exciting, but also dangerous: a close bond with the child that excludes and evades parental authority.

It's true that children themselves aren't always present in the pixie advertisements, but it's also fair to argue that they are assumed to be there: these adverts were created for them, so their gaze and responses are 'built in' as a virtual presence. Moreover, various symbolic factors lead the viewer to read this special relationship into the adverts, as culture has long configured a close bond between children and the supernatural. I've already referred to Diane Purkiss's research into the way both children and supernatural beings were felt to occupy the liminal zone of the 'not fully alive', and this affinity became charged with additional, sometimes contradictory, layers of meaning in Victorian Britain. Then the supernatural and childhood merged into a strange symbolic alliance, due to the fact that both represented values (play, irrationality, fancy) antithetical to the brutal new social and economic realities introduced by the industrial revolution. Purkiss joins up the narrative:

> The link between children and fairies came naturally.
> Children were associated with fairies anyway;
> childhood is a boundary of life, and many folktales,
> as the Victorians well knew, told of children stolen by fairies.
> Increasingly, the Victorians came to see such stories not as
> horrific abductions, but as signs that children and fairies
> were somehow akin.[4]

In denial of the reality of child labour and exploitation (although supporting efforts to end it), Victorian culture idealised images of children as completely 'non-functional' and 'non-productive': given over to dream, fantasy and vision, and closer to the portals of faerie than any adult.[5]

This affinity between child and supernatural goes even further, leading to an interchangeability between the two domains. Today, we see many examples of day crèches or children's clothing shops called 'Little Pixies' or 'Pixies': child and pixie are of the same world, and the boundaries between them are blurred. The same discourse is at work in contemporary New Age circles, which term supposedly psychically gifted children able to talk to spirits 'Indigo Children'. In fact, New Age discourse draws heavily on Romantic antecedents in seeing all children as special in their affinity with the supernatural:

> So next time your little one doesn't want to go to
> sleep because there is someone in their room, or
> when you hear them sitting by themselves, chatting
> away to an invisible friend, or even next time you see
> that shadow in the corner of your eye, stop and think
> about it for a moment. There may be such a thing as
> ghosts after all.[6]

Given this back story of close association between children and supernatural beings, it's possible to understand further why Snap, Crackle and Pop ally themselves with the child. It is even possible to argue that the trio represent the dimensions of childhood closed off to adulthood. The pixies may provide a metaphor for the human children in the household – and in fact, Snap, Crackle and Pop were originally created as a fairy-tale triad of brothers, superimposing figures of childhood onto their supernatural status from the start. But if they *are* children, they symbolise those aspects of childhood which are inaccessible to parents and adults.

That sense of inaccessibility and intra-familial division is deepened by the continued reverberations of another Victorian legacy: the idea that exclusion from contact with the supernatural was a defining feature of adulthood itself. Becoming an adult meant losing your ability to see and talk to supernatural beings. 'The idea that in growing old people lose the ability to see the fairies acquired enormous power in this period,' writes Nicola Bown.[7] Her observation is echoed by Purkiss, who notes that in Victorian Britain 'an inability to hear or see fairies is the mark of the adult'.[8]

In this way, the Victorians created a clear boundary line dividing childhood from adulthood – a boundary marked by, among other factors, whether or not you could see supernatural beings. The effect was to place a considerable burden on children: their role was to keep open the gates of other worlds, a task adults now felt unable to assume. In other words, it was emotionally important for adults to know that children believed in fairies.[9]

But, while the Rice Krispies adverts featuring Snap, Crackle and Pop reveal a clearly demarcated boundary between childhood and adulthood – and one in which the presence of pixies requires the absence of adults – they're not framed by adult fantasies and desires. Many adverts play on adult fantasies of childish cuteness and otherness; these don't. The pixies refuse to be assimilated into any kind of adult-approved framework; instead they offer the child the magical succour of fun, mischief and subversion defined against official familial power structures. Even when they purport to liaise with 'Mum' about nutrition, they strut around parodying the gestures of authority and televisual expertise. We can't take their attempt to be serious seriously (Fig. 3).

The old, sometimes ancient, fairy themes above provide a kind of unconscious context for interpreting what Snap, Crackle and Pop are up to in that suburban kitchen, just as they would have done for the adverts' original TV audience in the 1990s. The pixies create a symbolic rift in the family, defining the difference between parents and children, and furthermore their anarchic behaviour undermines parental authority, giving children models of resistance, subversion and imaginary freedom in the confined space of the suburban home.[10]

But, as the first decade of the 21st century unfolded and cultural values moved on, the pixies could not continue to play their trickster role. By separating parents from children, and usurping legitimate authority within the home, the pixies eventually came up against a changing moral climate in which these narratives became problematic.

The most obvious of these changes affected attitudes towards marketing to children. Since these adverts were aired in the 1990s, marketers and advertisers have faced increasing regulation in the way they're allowed to communicate child-orientated products. The codes they now endorse highlight the need to curb 'pester power', which inevitably means steering away from addressing children directly, and making sure no division is stirred up between them and their parents: 'advertising must not directly exhort children to buy a product or service'.[11] Different companies also write their own codes and principles to reflect and sometimes exceed the requirements of independent regulatory bodies. Unilever, for example, makes explicit not just that it will 'not encourage pester power', but also that it will 'not undermine parental influence'.

As outlined above, the pixies used to advertise Rice Krispies represent a very clear example of 'undermining parental influence'. And they do so in the best fairy-tale tradition of offering power to the powerless, chances to outwit authority, and a general overturning of traditional power structures.[13] This connection helps us see the attraction for advertisers: fairy-tale themes and characters offer particular seductions, those of autonomy and subversion, to relatively vulnerable and powerless audiences.

In other words, there are symbolic affinities between advertising in general and fairy tales. Examples like 'The Pied Piper of Hamelin' and 'Hansel and Gretel' show how commonly child seduction figures as a theme within fairy stories, as well as being an effect of the tales themselves. And if fairy tales display affinities with advertising's own quest to seduce and fascinate, the converse is also true: the world of the supernatural is far from innocent of themes of greed, profit and commerce (however much many Victorians wanted to see it as such). Christina Rossetti's 1859 poem 'The Goblin Market' explicitly couches the seduction of the supernatural in terms of commerce:

> Morning and evening
> Maids heard the goblins cry:
> *"Come buy our orchard fruits,*
> *Come buy, come buy [...]."*

Of course, the exploitation of children cannot be justified by a fairy-tale tradition, but it is worth pointing out the connections between seduction, subversion and fairy tale. These connections provide clues as to why Snap, Crackle and Pop have all but disappeared from Rice Krispies advertising. Today's more regulated and ethically-aware marketing climate has made the seductions of the supernatural much more culturally awkward.

Advertising regulations are only part of the story here. The sidelining of the pixies in Rice Krispies advertising reflects a wider cultural transition towards a more conservative promotion of family stability and unity. There are no simple political and social judgements to be made here: social desires to protect children from commercial exploitation have also been the occasion of a restatement of 'traditional family values'. While these are not necessarily related concerns, it's easy to see how they might dovetail. For instance, as we've seen, Unilever's wording of its advertising code includes a commitment 'not to undermine parental influence', protecting children but also opening the way to a restatement of more conservative notions of parental power and authority.

The idea that a third party, someone from outside the family, can speak directly to a child has also come under threat from wider social anxieties over child seduction. The thought of an outside voice intervening between parent and child with an alluring proposition now elicits heightened levels of suspicion. Whatever the nature of that seduction, deeper fears of the 'lurability' of the child still come into effect.

And yet, 'luring' is precisely what pixies and other sprites often do, with a whole host of unreliable 'special offers' from dangerous fairy food to illusory gold. Reviewing this complex mesh of factors – the ethics of child marketing, wider fears of child seduction, and nostalgic attempts to reinstate family structure – we can more fully understand why the fairy tale can no longer wreak its playful subversive magic in advertising as it used to do.

But what will replace it? Recent 'post-pixies' Rice Krispies advertising shows how some of the cultural anxieties described above are surfacing.

In 'Catching Sounds', a 2010 advert, a little boy catches the magical sound of the crackling cereal in his hands and passes it to his mum, surly teenage sister (who's not interested) and then to his pet hamster (Fig. 4). The still shows that a significant change has taken place in the symbolic landscape of advertising: from being absent, the mother is now central. And, of course, remembering the point made earlier about the mutually exclusive relationship between mother and pixies, the mother's central presence pushes the pixies to the sidelines.

In fact, the only time we see the pixies in this advert is at the end – the 'pack shot' moment. Far from careering around anarchically, they now only appear as two-dimensional illustrations on the box. Snap enjoys a brief flicker of animation at the end,[14] but it's no more than a passing flutter. And taking a closer look at the pixies' poses, we can see that they're in passive 'listening' mode, rather than being cheeky and riotous as they were before. Snap even urges children to be quiet so they can hear the crackle of the cereal (Fig. 5). So, from the explosive chaos of the 1990s adverts, there's been a complete turnaround: the pixies now urge controlled, quiet, 'good behaviour' from children.

A closer look at the child himself reveals that he's dressed in a typical child's outfit from the 1970s (I used to wear exactly the same clothes myself in those less gendered times!). His dungarees and Scandinavian knitwear don't feel in the least bit contemporary. It's not just a fashion oversight: his attire tells us that the advert is primarily targeted at the mother, likely herself to have been a child in the 1970s, and therefore likely to feel nostalgic for her own childhood on seeing this little boy (Fig. 6).

Fig. 4 Catching Sounds.
Fig.5 Catching Sounds.
Fig. 6 Catching Sounds.
Fig. 7 Catching Sounds.
Fig. 8 Mr Kipling.

Fig. 9 Sainsbury's.
Fig. 10 Rice Krispies – Beautiful Rain.
Fig. 11 John Lewis Christmas advert.
Fig. 12 John Lewis Christmas advert.

Because this nostalgic vision is clearly targeted at the 30- or 40-something mother, we can see the effects of the ban on 'pester power' in action: the advert now speaks to the mother, not to the child. So there's no more need to invoke the seductions of the supernatural, with its potential to overturn the order of the home. Now it's precisely that domestic order which the advert needs to protect and reinforce. The mood of Rice Krispies advertising has changed from anarchic magic to the secure, comforting nostalgia of a family scenario which doesn't seem to have changed since the 1970s.

This isn't just one brand's change in tone: it's part of a wider cultural transition towards nostalgia, order, and stasis, away from the seductions and subversions of fantasy. Mother and child are reunited in this advert; they're no longer kept apart by the secrets and divisions of supernatural intervention in the family home. There is a suggestion of family discord in the form of the sulky teenage sister, but her role is tangential. She's there to provide 'emotional authenticity' and to add a pinch of salt to an otherwise sweet dish (Fig. 7).

Despite this hint of dissent, the really important relationship – mother and child – has been restored to unity. A dream of domestic cohesion, anchored in the mother-child bond and unbroken inter-generational transmission (the 'passing on' of the Rice Krispies experience), has replaced the pixies and their troublesome ways.

So far, this article has explored various factors behind the sidelining of the pixies in Rice Krispies advertising and its implications for fantasy and fairy tale in consumer culture. There is one more major theme to examine in this regard: the quest, in mainstream British culture, for maximum emotional authenticity, and for a true flavour of 'everyday magic'.

These values are constructed in advertising through various executional devices: close-ups,[15] intimately lit domestic interiors (just like the one in 'Catching Sounds'), detail, texture and so on. The end goal is to create an intimate and real connection with ordinary life, showing that the advertiser 'shares' their audience's daily lives, rather than 'entertaining' them, which would imply too much separation and distance.

It's clear that this quest for 'everyday authenticity', even if it involves a romantic idea of the 'magic' of everyday moments, comes into conflict with fairy-tale and fantasy themes. When Rice Krispies presented its young audience with Snap, Crackle and Pop, its role was 'entertainer': the pixies' pranks and tricks were, in part, a show to delight and amuse the child.

But, as the cultural tide increasingly turns towards authenticity, many brands are now deserting their former 'magical' role as entertainers and conjurors of the fantastical. Instead, they want to be Vermeers, painting intimate domestic settings rich with emotionally compelling details. 'Catching Sounds' is typical of this new flavour. It reveals a love affair with ordinariness which leaves little room for pixies.

This tendency is currently gaining cultural traction. A book published earlier this year, *Embracing the Ordinary* by Michael Foley, strikes a resonant chord with its paean to the magic of everyday banality, whether that be domestic, corporate or urban.[16] The book takes the reader on long forays into Proust and Joyce, showing how they transfigured the banal everyday world into something magical and mysterious. It's fascinating to see how Foley's exploration of the banal stuff of everyday life reflects the way advertising is moving towards a glorification of the same theme.

Interestingly, Foley also celebrates Vermeer for his visions of intimate interiority suffused with the value of 'everydayness'.[17] Even where the visual language may not be absolutely identical, there are clear affinities between painters of bourgeois domesticity, like Vermeer, and the way many advertisers today try to affirm the values of authenticity and ordinariness in the depiction of the family home (Figs 8 and 9).

This new ethos in advertising and culture shrinks the space available for the expression of fantastic and fairy-tale themes. In fact, supernatural beings and worlds are excluded by this affirmation of the 'domestic everyday'. It's very much an ethic, as well as an aesthetic: in the images above, the life of the child is closely framed by the presence and care of the adult. It is this framing which prevents the possibility of other worlds, visions and creatures leaking into the family home.

As we've seen, culture has given the supernatural an important relationship with childhood, but that's not something easily shared with adults. So, for the child's imaginary friends to enter the scene, he or she needs some measure of alienation. Snap, Crackle and Pop were able to wreak havoc in a home already beset by a certain fracturedness: possibly parents at work, out, the child alone, maybe making their own breakfast, and in need of magical assistance. These are the conditions favourable for magic and fairy tale to do their work. But when advertising transitions towards the celebration of everyday intimacy, which involves restoring a sense of unity and proximity to the family, there's less space for the fantastic to creep in.

Another recent publication, this time in the business field, reinforces this sense of a shrinking space for fantastic themes in advertising and marketing. *Tell the Truth*, by Sue Unerman and Jonathan Salem Baskin, urges marketers to move away from trying to 'entertain' consumers with creative scenarios, and instead to try to share their everyday reality.[18] The authors don't explicitly assert authenticity against the worlds of magic, illusion and the fantastic, but the implication is there. Running through their book are repeated messages to forget the idea that marketing is about 'hype' (in other words, illusions, magic tricks and conjurings) and move towards 'truth' instead. 'Truth', for them, means the emotional and practical realities of consumers' lives, while communicating authentically involves sharing in these realities, not addressing an audience with fictions, fables and entertainments.

The book reflects transitions already taking place in the marketing and advertising world, such as the sidelining of Snap, Crackle and Pop, and it will inspire more marketers and advertisers to move in a similar direction. Of course, the adverts looked at as examples of this new interest in 'authenticity' are fictions in their own right: we've seen how authenticity is constructed through various aesthetic tricks and tropes, such as the close-up. They're still entertainment, and still seductive (even though they're using the seductions of nostalgia to lure adults, rather than the supernatural to attract children). But nevertheless, the pressure is on for brands to drop overt expressions of fantasy and magic, and instead to explore authenticity as a way of demonstrating intimate proximity to people's lives.

To bring this essay to a close, I'd like to discuss the most recent Rice Krispies advertisement (at the time of writing). 'Beautiful Rain' shows images of a rainy British summer holiday, with children trapped inside caravans and cars, bored and miserable (Fig. 10). Rice Krispies saves parents from the trials of the situation with a special 'rescue pack', which allows children to colour in the pixies on the front.

This advert demonstrates one further step in the direction of 'embracing ordinariness' and away from the world of magic and fairy tale. Until recently, it would have been rare to see rain in an advertisement. Advertising was traditionally the world of dreams and fantasies – where the sun always shone and magical transformations were always possible. So the very introduction of rain is a sign that this advert wants to take 'embracing the ordinary' to a heightened level.

Unsurprisingly, the pixies are nowhere to be seen. They do not rescue the child from boredom as they might have done in the past, but only appear as blank silhouettes to be coloured in. So, again, from being an expression of youthful anarchy and subversion (outwitting parents), the pixies have become a way to subdue them into 'good behaviour', quiet and controlled. From being the magical helper of the child, they've become the (very un-magical) helper of the parent. The Rice Krispies colouring-in pack brings to mind Diane Purkiss's comment on *The Flower Fairies Activity Book* – a comparable way of turning supernatural beings into ways of quietening the child and ensuring 'good behaviour' – which 'features pages of the kind of pencil-and-paper games that a "good", "quiet" child might use to keep herself amused'.[19] From anarchy to controlled, quiet behaviour, the pixies have come a long way since those days of playing chuck-the-krispie-through-the-toast-rack. Purkiss describes the Flower Fairies as a logo for the 'good middle-class girl'; could it be that Snap, Crackle and Pop are heading the same way?

This advert also brings to mind a similar example, equally striking in its transition from the fantastic to an embrace of ordinariness: last year's John Lewis Christmas advertisement. Here, we see a young boy counting down the days until Christmas, bored and impatient as he waits for the big day to arrive. The advert breaks radically with traditional Christmas advertising, usually overflowing with magical symbols and stories, by exploring themes of *ennui*, everyday banality and 'empty time' (Figs 11 and 12). These desolate images aim almost to shock when set against what we expect from Christmas advertising: children glutted on magic, dream, fantasy and joy. Of course, it's exactly this clash which allows the advertiser to lay claim to 'emotional authenticity', signalled through emotions which break with expected patterns.

So both these adverts, 'Beautiful Rain' from Rice Krispies and last year's Christmas advert from John Lewis, show us childhoods cut off from the magical succour with which advertising used to surround them. As we've seen, there are complex cultural and ethical reasons at the root of this development. Increased concern over the ethics of advertising to children has put pressure on advertisers to reinstate adult authority, appealing to parents through nostalgic images of family and home and leaving behind the subversive anarchy of magic and fantasy.

But there are also bigger cultural forces at work, beyond specific issues relating to marketing to children. The transition towards authenticity and realism spills beyond the bounds of advertising aesthetics to reflect a society increasingly fascinated by the minutiae of everyday life (with social media undoubtedly playing a huge role). Of course, fantasy plays a huge role in British cultural life – we only have to look at the huge anticipation surrounding the cinematic release of 'The Hobbit' to see that. But in advertising, while fantasy themes remain strong, cultural pressures have combined to push creative expression towards realism and authenticity. For this reason, I see the sidelining of Snap, Crackle and Pop as significant beyond specific developments in one brand's approach. Fantasy and magical themes won't be conjured away overnight in advertising, owing to their long-standing connections with consumer culture. But they no longer have the unproblematic status they once had – and that story tells us a lot about how culture is changing today.

. . . .

Louise Jolly

References

1. Diane Purkiss, *Troublesome Things: A History of Fairies and Fairy Stories* (London: Penguin, 2000), 154.
2. *Ibid.*, 66. This crucial insight adds a further resonance to Nicola Bown's point about fairies being loved by men but disliked by women in Victorian Britain. See *Fairies in Nineteenth-Century Art and Literature* (Cambridge: Cambridge University Press, 2001), 18.
3. *Ibid.*, 60.
4. *Ibid.*, 254.
5. Hugh Cunningham, *The Invention of Childhood* (London: BBC Books, 2006), 151. Cunningham tells us that the domain of the child was the spiritual realm of 'fancy', the imagination unfettered and uncontaminated by any contact with reality.
6. http://www.minti.com/parenting-advice/3899/Children-and-the-supernatural-An-invitation-to-sceptics/
7. Bown, 171.
8. Purkiss, 239.

9. This insight forms the backbone of Jacqueline Rose's work, *The Case of Peter Pan, or the Impossibility of Children's Fiction* (Philadelphia: University of Pennsylvania Press, 1984).

10. Hugh Cunningham describes lack of freedom as a defining feature of contemporary childhood. In the late 20th and early 21st centuries, 'their access to the world outside their own home was sharply diminished', he writes (p.231).

11. Clause 5.9, UK advertising codes as defined by the Committee of Advertising Practice (www.cap.org.uk).

12. http://www.unilever.com/sustainable-living/Respondingtostakeholderconcerns/marketing/. I've chosen Unilever as an example, rather than Rice Krispies manufacturer Kellogg's, because of the interest of its language here.

13. 'The liberating magic which the fairy tale has at its disposal does not bring nature into play in a mythical way, but points to its complicity with liberated man', writes Walter Benjamin in 'The Storyteller', *Illuminations* (London: Pimlico, 1999), 83-107, 101.

14. http://www.leoburnett.co.uk/our-work/kellogg/

15. For more on close-ups and authenticity in advertising, see my piece on 'Extimacy', http://www.semionaut.net/extimacy/

16. Michael Foley, *Embracing the Ordinary: Lessons from the Champions of Everyday Life* (London: Simon & Schuster, 2012).

17. *Ibid.*, 89-90.

18. *Tell the Truth: Honesty Is Your Most Powerful Marketing Tool*, Sue Unerman and Jonathan Salem Baskin (Dallas, Texas: BenBella Books, 2012).

19. Purkiss, 311.

ALLAN CUNNINGHAM
TRADITIONAL TALES
EDITED BY TIM KILLICK

E.A. Hornel,
'A Galloway Idyll',
cover image for
Traditional Tales.

A review of

Alan Cunningham:
Traditional Tales

Sophia Kingshill

Most of the tales in this collection first appeared in the *London Magazine* between January 1821 and June 1822. In July 1822 they were reprinted in two volumes, with some revisions and additions, under the title *Traditional Tales of the English and Scottish Peasantry*. The most recent edition, until now, was published in 1884, and this is thus the first reprint in well over a century. It is a handsome production, including two essays written by Cunningham to introduce the magazine versions of the stories, as well as Tim Killick's informative introduction, a useful glossary, and endnotes providing some historical and critical background.

Cunningham was born in Dumfriesshire, but his regional interest covered both sides of the Solway, and metaphorically too he was a borderline figure, neither strictly a collector nor exactly a creator. His poetry became known from Robert Cromek's *Remains of Nithsdale and Galloway Song* (1810), ostensibly a book of traditional ballads, but in fact consisting largely of Cunningham's compositions (as Cromek may have known from the outset, though this question was never definitively answered). The presentation of original or heavily doctored work as orally transmitted material was a technique that Cunningham used repeatedly. In *Traditional Tales*, his own verses appear in every story, generally described as an 'old ballad', a song 'still to be heard' in Cumberland, an 'ancient prophecy', and so on. He believed that his faking was undetectable: 'I could cheat a whole General Assembly of Antiquarians with my original manner of writing and forging ballads,' he declared in a letter to his brother. Elsewhere, however, he claimed that he was genuinely reproducing what he had heard. In his first introductory essay for the *London Magazine*, he asserted that 'In regard to all the more poetical communications of my friends, I imitated the scrupulous fidelity of that prince of editors, honest Joseph Ritson' – although five years later, in the introduction to his *Songs of Scotland* (1825), he was less keen to compare himself with Ritson, who he said 'doubted almost all that other men believed', and whose 'fastidiousness, and querulous regard for accuracy, did far more harm than [Thomas] Percy's rich and fruitful imagination'.

Imagination was clearly the quality that Cunningham most admired, and in retelling his tales, as Killick notes, he regarded himself as licensed to embellish at will, much as an oral storyteller would have been. Local tradition certainly supplied at least some of his material. Again from his preamble to *Songs of Scotland* comes an account of a youth's abduction by fairies and his sister's failure to rescue him, a straightforward variation on the Tamlane legend that Cunningham says he heard in childhood as having happened to a neighbouring family. In *Traditional Tales* this appears as 'Elphin Irving, the Fairies' Cupbearer', dolled up with romantic and personal detail that obscures more than it illuminates.

In most cases, we cannot compare Cunningham's unadorned sources with his elaborated version, and it can be hard to guess where 'tradition' ends and authorial intervention begins. His tale of 'The Haunted Ships' is cited in Wilbur Bassett's examination of maritime legends *Wander-Ships* (1917), during a discussion of cursed vessels, as 'one of the most interesting of all this group of stories'. Interesting it is, with its decayed wrecks explained as the remnants of phantom ships piloted by demons, but Cunningham's framing of the narrative in terms of personal experience – 'One fine harvest evening, I went on board the shallop of Richard Faulder' – is misleading to the unwary reader. I have myself been guilty of taking Cunningham's 'I' as a more reliable narrator than seems at all likely on reading the whole volume.

Cunningham's contemporaries applauded him, with reservations. Walter Scott's praise – 'A man of genius' – has a sting to follow: 'who only requires the tact of knowing when and where to stop'. James Hogg remarked in a similar vein that Cunningham's fancy 'was boundless; but it was the luxury of a rich garden over-run with rampant weeds'. Later assessments, in terms of folklore collection, have ranged from Bassett's enthusiasm to Richard Dorson's comment, in *The British Folklorists* (1968), that *Traditional Tales* 'might more accurately have been titled "Literary Tales Faintly Suggested by Oral Traditions"'. In *The Fairies in English Tradition and Literature* (1967), Katharine Briggs mentions him briefly but not dismissively, suggesting that he was one of the earliest exponents of 'first-hand research'. Tim Killick's balanced introduction gives both sides of the argument, allowing a new generation to make up their own minds about Cunningham's value as author and interpreter.

Editor: Tim Killick
Association for Scottish Literary Studies (2012), 416pp

. . . .

Sophia Kingshill

Sussex Centre for Folklore, Fairy Tales, and Fantasy

The heart of this project is a focus on the importance of fairy tales as a creative force in literature and culture.

Literary fairy tales can be seen to mediate between folktales, from which they often derive form and content, and the more elaborate narratives of fantasy novels. We provide a forum for writers and scholars from various disciplines to discuss folk narratives, fairy tales, and fantasy works, as independent genres and in terms of the resonances and dissonances between them and other cultural forms.

The founding impulse for the Centre is related to the specific locale of Sussex and its surrounding region, an area rich in authors and illustrators across the three kinds of narrative. However, the planned scope of research is national and international, bringing together writers and scholars, as well as publishing and curating scholarly resources, from around the globe. The fairy-tale tradition that shapes fantasy derives its sources from Europe and beyond. It is the diversity and exuberance of folktales, fairy tales, and the fantastic imagination that we seek to explore, discuss, and celebrate.

Our activities include:
- The Folktales mailing list, moderated by the Centre
- An annual international conference
- The creation of the Sussex Folklore Index, a digital bibliographic resource
- A programme of events, performances, and exhibitions
- The publication of a regular newsletter and the biannual Centre Journal, *Gramarye*
- Collaboration with international scholars in the fields of fairy tales, folklore, and fantasy

Find out more
Visit www.chi.ac.uk/scfff or email b.gray@chi.ac.uk.

A review of

The Place of Lewis Carroll in Children's Literature

Colin Manlove

In this often highly detailed book Professor Susina considers Lewis Carroll's work from a variety of standpoints – his juvenilia, his place in the Victorian literary fairy-tale tradition, the role of letters in the *Alice* books, his creation of an *Alice* books industry, his many illustrators, his photography, his class prejudice, the many imitations of *Alice*, boundary-crossing in *Sylvie and Bruno*, the marketing of *Alice* in recent times, *Alice* as a possible hyper-text and Jon Scieszka's *Walt Disney's Alice in Wonderland* (2008).

Susina well conveys just how much the *Alice* books are a unique synthesis of Carroll and Tenniel, of text and illustrations and how the one cannot exist without the other. In particular he shows how Carroll, as a devotee of children's pantomime, created the *Alice* books as a series of highly visualised tableaux that stimulated Tenniel to his own inspired recreations. Susina also shows how Carroll was one of the first authors to attend continuously to the marketing of his books, continually adapting *Alice* to different modes, whether nursery book or magic lantern slide shows or even pursuing literary spin-offs, such as Savile Clarke's *Alice in Wonderland: A Musical Dream play* (1886); and bringing about, with *The Hunting of the Snark* (1876), the first use of a dust jacket which could give laudatory blurbs and mentions of his other books.

In his examination of *Sylvie and Bruno*, and his consideration of *Alice*'s continued popularity as a hyper-text, Susina is undoubtedly original. With *Sylvie and Bruno* his remarks on the limited application of the Fortunatus' purse image in the book are well made, and his idea that the explosion of the Professor's confused chemical bottles is a figure of Carroll's own intuition that the book did not hold together is convincing. When he quotes Mein Herr saying of the purse that makes a moebius strip, "Whatever is *inside* that purse is *outside* it; and whatever is *outside* it, is *inside* it", the application may be as much to the reflection of the imagination and the world, or dreaming and reality, as described by Novalis, 'Was außer mir ist, ist gerade in mir, ist mein; und umgekehrt' (*Die Fragmente*; Carroll may well have been led to Novalis by his friend George MacDonald, who was much influenced by this writer.) This would give point to the use of a 'Mein Herr' here, and also to the relation between dreaming and reality in *Sylvie and Bruno* as a whole.

Professor Susina's knowledge of the modern computerised use of hyper-texts, or interactive books on disc, in children's literature is compendious; and his analysis of why *Alice in Wonderland*, despite the many hyper-texts created out of it, is not done full justice by this medium is convincing. For all its episodic character, which lends itself to hyper-textual form, the story in *Alice* still remains linear and resistant to being shuffled about. Further, hyper-texts lose Carroll's controlling authorial voice which is an essential part of the experience of the book. And so far they have been poor at integrating the text and Tenniel's drawings, which are either out of place or not even present. Susina finds more successful a hyper-text that acts as a re-creation rather than a translation of *Alice* – Cyan, Inc.'s *Manhole* (1992). But he has to conclude that the hyper-text versions of *Alice* to date 'reveal limitations of creating a new version that is as compelling or well-designed as Carroll's original book'.

Susina is perhaps less penetrating in his account of the place of *Alice* in the Victorian literary fairy-tale tradition, where writers from Harvey Darton onwards have put Carroll alongside Elizabeth Sinclair, F.E. Paget, Ruskin, Thackeray and Kingsley. And though Susina claims that Carroll was indebted to all these writers, and highly so to Kingsley, he somehow never proves this; when he comes to Kingsley, he points out only how *Alice* differs from *The Water-Babies*. Generally Susina's book does not provide enough in the way of literary analysis.

We are told in the Acknowledgements that 'Many of these essays first began as conference papers', and it does show. The relevance to the broad topic of Carroll's place in children's literature is often tenuous, and one has the impression that many topics are pursued for their own sake. There is repetition of points, showing both the absence of a continuously argued central theme, and the lack of a thorough re-reading and reworking before publication of the separate papers that make up the book. However, there is a broad topic behind all the chapters, which is the issue of the continuing survival and relevance of Carroll's work both in its time and down to our own day. Susina, it must be said, is not overly optimistic about the future of Carroll's work. In an engaging Afterword he describes his worry about introducing *Alice in Wonderland* to his son, and shows how he managed to do so only by indirection, when one day the two of them had been laughing over puns and he could lead on to those in *Alice*.

Author: Jan Susina
Routledge (New York and London, 2010), 232pp

. . . .

Colin Manlove

A review of

Bringing Light to Twilight: Perspectives on the Pop Culture Phenomenon

Malini Roy

I was in disbelief that I'd just explained my dreary life to this bizarre, beautiful boy who may or may not despise me.

Meyer, Twilight

A human girl having a vampire boyfriend feels 'bizarre' enough; placing the vampire on moral high ground, whence he might 'despise' the human, insane. Yet, the commonplace Bella's desire for the 'beautiful' vampire Edward has made for a bold fantasy come real, forming the absurd yet bestselling premise of *Twilight* – the well-known series of four novels for young adults by Stephenie Meyer, published 2005 onwards, and complemented by films and franchise to boot. This 'Pop Culture Phenomenon' is addressed comprehensively by *Bringing Light to Twilight*. Edited by Giselle Liza Anatol, this scholarly essay collection illumines and mobilises critical understanding of the *Twilight* phenomenon as a cardinal element and determinant of contemporary globalised American youth culture.

Bringing Light offers a valuable critical intervention in the burgeoning field of scholarly books and articles on *Twilight*, and benefits from a breadth of perspectives. The collection's sixteen essays cover a range and variety of schools of criticism, analysing the *Twilight* phenomenon through the lenses of folklore and fairy tale, gender and sexuality, queer theory, Gothic literature and subcultures, vampire literature, popular culture, translation, fan fiction, law, theology, Marxist theory, race and diaspora, and environmental studies.

One of the noteworthy features of this collection, to scholars and students of *Twilight*, is the mélange of competing perspectives on the source material emerging through the varied approaches of the essays, unpacking interpretative richness in a series often dismissed as 'insipid,' 'vapid,' 'shallow,' and 'sexist' (4). This potpourri of perspectives is discernible, for instance, in multiple and contested readings of Bella's voluntary identity change from human to Edward's vampirical state, a transformation that gains her the vampire's immortality and omnipotency, but loses her the human moral ace of possessing a soul. For Kristina Deffenbacher and Mikayla Zagoria-Moffet, who evaluate the intertextual links of *Twilight* with *Jane Eyre*, Bella's transformation is a celebratory act of sexual empowerment, winning for her 'the ability to throw off traditional, normative gender expectations and overcome repeated instances of women's victimization' (34). Meredith Wallis, whose essay identifies *Twilight* in terms of its legal forms and meaning, inflects the transformation into a zone of deep ambivalence: Edward perceives his own 'consensual transition to vampirism as one of damnation' — hence Bella's 'consenting' and 'overwhelming desire' for the transformation is doubly culpable (92). Tammy Dietz, writing in the academically unusual format of the personal memoir, offers a vigorous reading of Bella's transformation as a dangerous act of self-abdication that rings a death-knell for women's collective aspirations for 'their own personal development in life' (108).

Readers interested in Gothic and vampire literature generally will find the collection informative in assessing the position of *Twilight* in the history of vampire literature and in contemporary vampire culture, as expressed in cinema, tourism, and style and fashion. Anatol's introduction grounds the three recognisable — if discontinuous — waves of vampire literature, from late Romantic and Victorian instances through 20th- and 21st-century descendants, noting the surprising but decisive presence of the vampire in contemporary children's literature, including Neil Gaiman's recent Newbery-winning *The Graveyard Book*. Anatol's essay with Joo Ok Kim develops this genealogy, identifying Bella's subject position as human ethnographer of the non-normative vampires and werewolves in the series. Bella is considered as an inheritor of Jonathan Harker in Bram Stoker's *Dracula*; Harker's Englishness places him at the centre of a cultural mindset that exoticises the blood-drinking Eastern European Count. Other essays in the collection consider the gender politics of *Twilight* in relation to celebrated representations of vampires in contemporary book and television series. Contrasting *Twilight* with *Buffy the Vampire Slayer*, Rhonda Nicol cleverly inverts common popular associations of Buffy as feminist icon of 'girl power' and Bella as the reactionary good girl, by revealing Buffy's alignment with the problematic aspects of Third-Wave feminism that privilege sexual liberation for women without the corresponding socio-economic empowerment.

The collection thus succeeds in creating a timely exposé of the 'ideological constructs underlying' the *Twilight* texts, an aim captured airily in the assonantal flourish of the collection's title — *Bringing Light to Twilight*. This commitment towards critical reading of the *Twilight* phenomenon underpins the editor's hope that the collection will be read not only in 'university settings' but also 'outside the academy' (2). This instrumental aim, laudable in terms of demystifying a series known to elicit a faddish following, provides a living instance of the socially useful purpose that the humanities can serve, particularly in a post-recession era that has become particularly grudging towards the institutional study of literature and the arts. Unfortunately, this potential for reaching out to the wider public appears to be undone by the somewhat patronising note struck by the book's title, with its hint of a snarky desire to enlighten consumers of *Twilight* about a meretricious popular phenomenon. This attitude of superiority is perhaps understandable as a bid for leverage in an academic establishment that often positions popular culture studies as poor cousin. But in this case, ivory-tower snobbery may have had the counterproductive effect of foreclosing potentially interesting avenues of enquiry, such as the rhetorical or narrative strategies that make Meyer's prose enchanting for many. Kim Allen Gleed's essay, for instance, which locates in Luc Rigoureau's French translation of *Twilight* a text more evocative than the original, also appears to indicate a more judicious choice of words and phrases by Meyer than is usually presumed. But the focus here on the reception of *Twilight* leaves the ur-text less than its due.

Editor: Giselle Liza Anatol
Palgrave Macmillan (2011), 248pp

. . . .

Malini Roy

Thresholds

Home of the International Postgraduate Short Story Forum.
Cross the threshold, join the conversation ...

Like doorways and other thresholds, a great short story lets us step into lives, across worlds and through states of mind. Whether you're a postgraduate student with a love of the short story, a curious reader or a short story writer, register at THRESHOLDS now to find out more and join the conversation.

www.chi.ac.uk/shortstoryforum

A review of

On Monsters:
An Unnatural History
of Our Worst Fears

Miles Leeson

Being unfamiliar with Asma's work previous to this new monograph I undertook a little research to discover more and was both impressed and surprised to find that he is what we might term a 'celebrity' academic of sorts, with numerous publications on a variety of subjects that meld the philosophy of mind, general science writing and cultural discussion. Normally an academic writer has to wait a rather long time for reviews considering the impact of one's work on one's peers – in some cases up to two years. Asma has no such issue here as the *Washington Post*, the *Telegraph*, the *New York Times* and a range of other international publications have already offered positive feedback and promoted his work to a far wider audience than any subject-specific journal ever could. This review focuses on Asma's intended audience – academics with a deep love of the fantastic and imaginary.

So does Asma's work offer a new, enhancing vision of the monstrous in fiction or a collection of various thoughts on, as he puts it, 'an unnatural history'? Firstly there is much to praise, as the remit Asma has given himself is vast. Not only does he move across continents, time and cultures, but between the imaginary, the fictive and the 'real' – or rather the historical. The book has the feel of a collection of the grotesque – indeed some of the accompanying pictures are both uncanny and chilling in equal measure – and the movement between, say, Freud, torture porn and creeping flesh segue well. Chapter titles such as 'The Monster Killer', 'Darwin's Mutants', and 'The Art of Human Vulnerability: Angst and Horror' are just a taste of what Asma has in store for us.

Having said this, there is a case to be made that this is a monstrous banquet of overindulgence which may well leave the reader feeling rather dissipated. This is certainly not a book to be read in one sitting nor one that goes deep into the dark heart of 'monsterism'; the material provided is, perhaps, nothing new (unless Asma's alchemy with the 'real' and the fantastic is considered) and this may dissuade the likely reader of *Gramarye*. At times there is a sense of superficiality to it that is lacking in other, perhaps more academic, monographs on singular aspects of fantasy and the monstrous, and the ground covered – as a piece of cultural history perhaps – may not be to everyone's taste. At times themes are left hanging and I wanted to hear more on a specific idea but was soon moved on to notice the similarities between, for example, attitudes to deformed humans and the policies of the Khmer Rouge. It is certainly an example of what Tolkien called the 'bubbling pot of faerie', and ladles of monstrous broth are offered with a dash of cultural history and a *soupçon* of sociological theory.

But does this approach work? It is unlikely that this book will be returned to time and again for in-depth study but, for those working in this area, it may well be a useful first reference point when refreshing one's mind or uncovering a new subject area. Asma has given us a preliminary sketch only and presents to a range of academic disciplines the outline for new and original research opportunities.

It would be wrong for an academic reader to dismiss this book for its perhaps overly populist approach as there is much here that, if taken in small amounts, has the ability to engage and inspire. The most important contribution of the book is to reflect the darkness of monsters back towards the creator – the storyteller – and ask why it is that humanity's darkness must always be told and retold.

Author: Stephen T. Asma
Oxford University Press (USA, 2011), 368pp

. . . .

Miles Leeson

About the contributors

William Gray
Bill Gray, Professor of Literary History and Hermeneutics at the University of Chichester, is the founder of the Sussex Centre for Folklore, Fairy Tales and Fantasy. He studied literature, philosophy and theology at the universities of Oxford, Edinburgh and Princeton, and has published articles and chapters in all of these areas, as well as books on C.S. Lewis and Robert Louis Stevenson. Gray has recently published three books on fantasy: *Fantasy, Myth and the Measure of Truth: Tales of Pullman, Lewis, Tolkien, MacDonald and Hoffmann, Death and Fantasy* and *Fantasy, Art and Life*. He is currently working on an edition of Robert Louis Stevenson's *Fables & Fairy Tales* for Edinburgh University Press.

Nicholas Tucker
Nicholas Tucker lives in Lewes and was a teacher and educational psychologist before lecturing in Cultural Studies at the University of Sussex. He is the author of five books about children, childhood and reading, including *The Rough Guides to Children's Books* – 0-5 and 5-11 – with a third volume on teenage reading to be published later this year. He has also written six books for children, broadcasts frequently and reviews widely in the national press. However, most of what he has learned about children's literature over the years has come from reading to his three children, and now to their children as well.

Jacqueline Simpson
Professor Jacqueline Simpson studied English Literature and Medieval Icelandic at the University of London. She is the Sussex Centre's Visiting Professor of Folklore and has also been, at various times, Editor, Secretary, and President of the Folklore Society. Her published works include *A Dictionary of English Folklore* (with Steve Roud), *British Dragons, European Mythology, Folklore of Sussex, Folklore of the Welsh Border, Green Men and White Swans: The Folklore of British Pub Names, The Lore of the Land: A Guide to England's Legends, from Spring-heeled Jack to the Witches of Warboys* (with Jennifer Westwood), and *The Folklore of the Discworld* (with Terry Pratchett).

Anne Anderson

Dr Anne Anderson is an Hon. Research Fellow at the University of Exeter, an Associate of the Leeds Centre for Victorian Studies and Fellow of the Henry Francis Du Pont Museum and Library, Winterthur, Delaware. International speaker, broadcaster and writer, Anne was a senior lecturer in the History of Art and Design at Southampton Solent University for 14 years. She has authored many academic papers in leading journals and curated two national exhibitions, *Ancient Landscape*, *Pastoral Visions* and *The Truth about Faeries*.

Brian Froud

Brian Froud has been an internationally renowned and bestselling faerie artist and an authority on faeries and faerie lore for over 35 years. His international best-selling book, *Faeries*, with fantasy illustrator Alan Lee, is a modern classic of art and British fairy folklore, while his cult hit movies with Jim Henson, the 'Dark Crystal' and 'Labyrinth', set new standards for design, puppeteering and animatronics. With over 8 million books sold to date, Brian's international best sellers include the *Lady Cottington's Pressed Fairy Album* series with Monty Python's Terry Jones and Prof. Ari Berk, *Good Faeries/Bad Faeries*, and the *Faeries Oracle*, and collaborations with Prof. Ari Berk on *Goblins!*, the *Runes of Elfland* and *Brian Froud's World of Faerie*. Two festival events, Faerieworlds and FaerieCon, are held in his honour and attract over 30,000 guests each year. His latest book, *Trolls*, is available now. Brian lives in Devon, England, with his wife, internationally acclaimed doll maker Wendy Froud.

Heather Robbins

Heather Robbins is the Assistant for the Sussex Centre for Folklore, Fairy Tales and Fantasy. Her lifelong appreciation of these themes was strengthened during her studies of German fantasy writers for her Masters in Modern Languages at the University of Manchester. She loves Victorian fantasy and has greatly enjoyed helping Professor Bill Gray with his research on Robert Louis Stevenson's *Fables and Fairy Tales*, using original manuscripts. She was previously Commissioning Editor of local history at Phillimore publishers.

Angelika H. Rüdiger

Dr Angelika H. Rüdiger obtained a degree in Chemistry at the University of Tübingen (Germany) in 1991. In 1996, she was awarded the title of "Dr. rer. nat" (*summa cum laude*) by the University of Braunschweig. A mother of three daughters, she moved into teaching in 2006. She currently teaches chemistry and physics at the Philipp-Matthäus-Hahn Schule, Nürtingen, Germany, in parallel to her part-time postgraduate studies at the Department of Welsh, University of Bangor.

Kate Forsyth

Kate Forsyth is an Australian fantasy author best known for the *Witches of Eileanan* series, and the *Rhiannon's Ride* series, which is also set in Eileanan. She is the author of several children's fantasy books, including *The Gypsy Crown*, *The Starthorn Tree*, *Dragon Gold* and *Wishing For Trouble*. She is an internationally published poet with a collection called *Radiance*, and a five-time Aurealis Award winner.

Martine Hennard Dutheil de la Rochère

Dr Martine Hennard Dutheil de la Rochère teaches modern English and comparative literature at the University of Lausanne, Switzerland, where she was Associate Dean of the Humanities from 2007 to 2010. Her research interests include various aspects of modern and contemporary literature, especially postcolonial and postmodern fiction, fairy tale rewritings and translation studies. She is the author of *Origin and Originality in Salman Rushdie's Fiction* (1999) and co-editor of *Satan and After* (2010) and *Des Fata aux fées: regards croisés de l'Antiquité à nos jours* (2011). She has published essays in *Dickens in Europe*, *Conrad's Heart of Darkness and Contemporary Thought*, *La Retraduction*, *Fairy Tales Reimagined*, *Postcolonial Ghosts*, *The Seeming and the Seen*, *Dickens Studies Annual*, *Critical Essays on Salman Rushdie* and various journals, including *MFS*, *Dickens Quarterly*, *College Literature*, *EJES*, *Conradiana*, *The Conradian*, *Palimpsestes*, *JSSE* and *Marvels & Tales*. Her book on the interplay of translation and rewriting in Angela Carter's short fiction is forthcoming.

Steve O'Brien

Dr Steve O'Brien is Senior Lecturer and Course Leader of the University of Portsmouth's MA in Creative Writing. He is an acclaimed poet and writer; his first collection of poems *Dark Hill Dreams* was published in 2006, and *Scrying Stone* in 2010. His research interests centre around the establishment of a coherent direction for Creative Writing pedagogy, in which the critical and creative registers of writing can be synthesised. He is the editor of the *London Magazine* (Britain's oldest literary journal). 'Herne' is taken from his upcoming work, *The Oldest Tales*, to be published by Greenwich Exchange Press.

Louise Jolly

Dr Louise Jolly's work straddles commercial and academic fields. In the course of her academic career, she completed a PhD at London University, which explored the persistence of Romantic themes in the growing consumer culture of 19th-century Paris. While researching her thesis, she also worked as a copywriter, giving her an exposure to commercial rhetoric and symbolism which offered much food for thought. Today she works as a writer and analyst in marketing and advertising, while pursuing wider interests in philosophy, cultural studies and literature.

Sophia Kingshill

Sophia Kingshill is co-author, with the late Jennifer Westwood, of *The Lore of Scotland* (Random House, 2009) and *The Fabled Coast* (Random House, 2012), a book of British and Irish sea legends. She also writes for the theatre. Her play *Do You Know This Man?* won the International One-Act Play Competition, and was produced in several theatres in Scotland. For many years she worked with Norwegian company Teater X, who performed her work at venues including the National Theatre in Bergen, the Åpne Teater in Oslo, and on national tours. She lives in London.

Colin Manlove
Dr Colin Manlove is a literary critic with a particular interest in fantasy. His *Modern Fantasy: Five Studies* (1975), which considers at length works by Charles Kingsley, George MacDonald, C.S. Lewis, J.R.R. Tolkien and Mervyn Peake, was written at a time when 'no serious study of the subject [of fantasy literature] has appeared' (Preface, p.vii). He has since written, among others, *Literature and Reality 1600-1800* (1978), *The Gap in Shakespeare: The Motif of Division from Richard II to The Tempest* (1981), *The Impulse of Fantasy Literature* (1982), *Science Fiction: Ten Explorations* (1986), *C S Lewis: His Literary Achievement* (1987), *Critical Thinking: A Guide to Interpreting Literary Texts* (1989), *Christian Fantasy: From 1200 to the Present* (1992), *The Chronicles of Narnia: The Patterning of a Fantastic World* (1993), *Scottish Fantasy Literature: A Critical Survey* (1994), *The Fantasy Literature of England* (1999) and *From Alice to Harry Potter: Children's Fantasy in England* (2003), and *The Order of Harry Potter: Literary Skill in the Hogwarts Epic* (2010). He was a lecturer in English Literature at the University of Edinburgh until his retirement in 1993.

Malini Roy
Dr Malini Roy was Research Administrator at the Sussex Centre for Folklore, Fairy Tales and Fantasy in 2009-10. She has published on the literary history of childhood, including a chapter in the essay collection *International Receptions of the Brothers Grimm*, eds Gillian Lathey and Vanessa Joosen (forthcoming 2012). Her doctoral work (Oxford University, 2008) explored representations of the child in the Romantic-era writings of Mary Wollstonecraft, William Godwin, and Mary and Percy Bysshe Shelley. Her other research interests include contemporary South Asian children's literature, and she has written a graphic novel adaptation of *Hamlet* for young adults (New Delhi: Campfire, forthcoming 2012).

Miles Leeson
Dr Miles Leeson is an Associate Lecturer in English at the University of Chichester. He studied for a DPhil at the University of Sussex and has previously taught at Sussex and the University of Portsmouth. He is currently completing work on his second monograph, *Beings in Time: The Philosophical Novelist in the Twentieth Century*, to be published by Bloomsbury in 2013, as well as an edited collection focusing on taboo and incest literature with Emma Miller from the University of Durham.

List of illustrations

We are grateful to the artists for their kind permission to use their work.

Gramarye

The Journal of the Sussex Centre for Folklore, Fairy Tales and Fantasy

We hope that you have enjoyed the second issue.

We welcome your comments and suggestions, which Bill Gray will be happy to receive at b.gray@chi.ac.uk.

Issue 3 of *Gramarye* will offer a similar mix of in-depth analysis, reviews, and commentary. To reserve your copy of *Gramarye* Issue 3, please contact Heather Robbins at h.robbins@chi.ac.uk.

We invite the submission of articles to peer review for inclusion in future issues of *Gramarye*. Your work should resonate with the main aim of the Centre, which is to provide writers and scholars from various disciplines with a forum to discuss folk narratives, fairy tales, and fantasy works, as independent genres and in terms of the resonances and dissonances between them and other cultural forms. Please refer to the Submission Guidelines on page 93 and send any queries to Bill Gray at b.gray@chi.ac.uk.

www.chi.ac.uk/scfff